THE
HEALTHY
CATERING
MANUAL

For Caroline Walker,
friend, colleague,
nutritionist, and relentless
pursuer of a national
diet worth eating.
Born 1950, died 1988.

THE
HEALTHY
CATERING
MANUAL

Christopher Robbins

*Published in
Association with
Evian natural
mineral water*

DK

DORLING KINDERSLEY, LONDON

A Jill Norman Book

First published in Great Britain in 1989
by Dorling Kindersley Limited,
9 Henrietta Street, London WC2E 8PS

British Library Cataloguing in Publication Data

Robbins, Christopher, *1946 Dec. 31*
The healthy catering manual.
1. Food science – For catering
I. Title
641.1'024642

ISBN 0-86318-327-1

Typeset in Great Britain by
Rowland Phototypesetting Limited
Bury St Edmunds, Suffolk
Printed and bound in Great Britain by
William Collins Sons & Co. Limited, Glasgow

CONTENTS

PREFACE

Evian-les-Bains, the home of Evian natural mineral water has been known as a health resort for two centuries, and today its familiar mineral water from the Alps is sold in more than 80 countries.

In the UK, distributors of Evian mineral water, Evian (Agencies) Ltd, are very aware of the importance of water for health and fitness. Water, after all, plays a very important part in our lives from the moment we are conceived. Seventy per cent of the average human body consists of water, and helps to fulfil many functions from temperature control to food digestion and elimination.

Evian pure mineral water is ideal to maintain a healthy fluid level, and, as it is such a lightly mineralised water it is easy to digest, and can safely be taken by those on a salt-free diet.

It is not surprising therefore that Evian takes such a great interest in health; healthy eating in particular. So much so that in 1986 Evian teamed up with *Caterer & Hotelkeeper* magazine to initiate the Healthy Menu of the Year Award, spearheading the move for caterers to become more aware of the food they serve to their customers.

In supporting this book, Evian hopes to further promote the cause of good health in catering establishments of all types and that it will prove to be an invaluable aid in offering your customers a healthier future.

CHAPTER ONE

THE ROLE
OF
CATERERS
IN HEALTH

*"To invite anyone is to
charge ourselves with his
happiness all the time he is
under our roof."*
BRILLAT SAVARIN

Caterers have a major role in the nation's health. From school meals, through works' canteens and seaside bed-and-breakfasts, from high street take-aways to high class restaurants like Leith's or the Ritz, caterers supply at least 20 per cent of all food eaten in the UK.

From school age until retirement, at least one week-day meal is taken out of the home by many in the population. This means that five out of the twenty-one main meals in a week are prepared by caterers. Allowing only a further two leisure meals out during evenings would mean nearly 30 per cent of all meals eaten come from some type of caterer. But as these meals are most often main meals like lunch or the evening meal, they contribute even more than 30 per cent to the total amount of food eaten day-in, week-out.

At present meals out of the home are among the most unhealthy eaten. They tend to contain more fat, sugar and salt than home-cooked foods, and fast foods particularly are usually lower in fibre and vitamins than home-cooked food. There are shining examples of healthy catering but these are the minority in a large and varied industry.

EVERY MEAL COUNTS

One of the most unhelpful 'old sayings' for caterers is, 'There are no bad foods, only bad diets.' This unscientific notion encourages caterers to believe that it is all right to serve fatty or sugary dishes and menus because their ill-effects will be more than made up by the rest of the customer's diet. This is bad practice. Of course every meal counts, although this does not mean that every meal must be a perfect nutritional mix.

The opponents of dietary change argue that there are 'no bad foods' in defence of foods like butter, fatty meats, sugar and sugary drinks which dietitians usually advise eating less of. The same people, often from food manufacturers or their promotion campaigns, seem happy to identify 'good foods' like full-fat milk, eggs and even butter. One leaflet from the old Egg Authority says eggs are so good that one should be eaten with every meal and the 'Drink a pint a day' slogan for milk left no doubt about the 'goodness' of milk. It is interesting that the 'bad foods' are those we are advised to eat less of whereas 'good foods' are those the food industry would like us to eat more of.

It is easy to compile a list of good foods which would be generally agreed; apples, fish, potatoes, wholemeal bread, dried apricots, etc. And of course it is as easy to find foods which are generally seen as bad for health: confectionery, lard, soggy chips, cream, most cooked puddings. Just as calling foods 'good for health' doesn't mean that only those foods should be eaten, there is no suggestion that 'bad foods' should never be eaten. The sensible action is to eat more of the good foods and less of the bad. This is a very useful attitude for caterers planning to improve the health rating of their food.

HEALTHY DOESN'T MEAN DIFFERENT

Healthy food can be normal food. The idea that the only way to eat a healthy diet was to eat lentils, brown rice and muesli at every meal has died, as it deserved. There is no reason why the average British diet can't be healthy without making radical changes to how people eat. Dishes like shepherd's pie, hamburgers and even chips can be made healthier and still keep their usual taste and appearance: there is no shortage of caterers or customers who would even say they are improved.

WHO DECIDES ON HEALTHY FOODS?

Many caterers feel it is not for them to impose healthy eating on their customers and some argue that they only provide what their customers demand. Of course, customers must be happy to eat at least some of the food on offer or tables would soon be empty. Customers also make choices from the options on the menu. *But they can only choose from what the caterer has decided to offer.*

The underlying dilemma is the customer's 'right to choose'. In theory it sounds right and proper that customers choose and caterers provide, but how well does this match what happens in practice? Does it conflict with introducing healthy catering?

Part of the confusion over choice may arise in the approach taken by standard catering text books. Kinton and Ceserani begin their discussion on menus in *The Theory of Catering* by saying, 'The aim is to give the customer what he wants and not what the caterer thinks the customer wants.' It is obvious that few caterers would be in business if they gave each customer *everything* that they wanted. There would be no point in having menus and both storekeeping and the kitchens would be chaos. Surely the valued skill of the caterer is in choosing dishes and menus that customers are happy to accept. Remember that chefs like Anton Mosimann and Raymond Blanc are famous and respected because of the choices they make for their customers who, it is worth adding, return time and time again to eat what the chef has decided goes on and in the menu! If the Dorchester clients are happy to be so treated, why expect less of your own customers?

Every day caterers make decisions on behalf of their customers. Consider the planning and decisions that are part of a caterer's daily job. Long before the customer arrives, caterers decide the menu, select the type and quality of meat or fish, the vegetables as well as all other ingredients to be used, decide on preparation and cooking methods and finally decide how dishes are to be presented at table. All these decisions are made without any involvement of the customer. Customer choice is restricted to making 'selections' from the dishes the caterer has chosen to place on the menu. There is not much difference in choice between *table d'hôte* and *à la carte* menus either. The latter offers more freedom to combine 'selections' but in both types of menu, choice is limited to what is on the menu. The more the food is enjoyed, the more profit rather than loss and the more the caterer is congratulated for the choices made on behalf of customers!

Customers' ability to exercise choices is restricted also by what is offered. Menus rarely provide information on the type of ingredients used or on their quality – the percentage of fat in the meat, the type of frying oil, how long before were the vegetables cooked, etc.? These details may seem petty or even irrelevant to some caterers, but if the customer is to have the right to choose and wants to eat healthily, these are obvious and important items of information.

Of course there is no suggestion that caterers daily force their will on captured customers. The fact is that the caterer's role includes making very important choices on behalf of customers. Real customer choice does occur at the table with preferences for certain dishes over others on the menu and, in the extreme, by customers going elsewhere if the food is neither of the type wanted nor up to the standard expected.

There is no reason why deciding to make food healthier should be seen differently from the normal responsibilities of caterers. Who would consider it an unfair imposition on customers to insist on only the best and freshest Scottish salmon in the market? Why should insisting on the healthiest of ingredients be any different? At the simplest, healthy decisions may mean buying leaner mince, using thinner batter for frying fish or scampi, grilling instead of frying, not adding MSG or cutting down on the salt in vegetable cooking water and stocks. The more imaginative might introduce a salad bar, begin offering new dishes which are interesting and healthy, or start indicating the fat or calorie content alongside dishes wherever menus are displayed. Who would consider these ideas worthy of complaint?

TRUST AND PROFESSIONAL STATUS

People don't eat only to take their appetites away. When any customer enters a restaurant, canteen or take-away, there is an implicit trust placed in the kitchen staff. Although it is normal for customers to have no knowledge of what goes on behind those kitchen doors or the counter, they trust that their food will be enjoyable, hygienic and value for money. Successful establishments satisfy their customers and have good reputations which confirm this trust.

It is interesting how uncommon it still is for healthy eating to feature in decisions taken on either side of the counter, except in specialist health-food restaurants and take-away outlets. But public attitudes are changing, and fast. They have had dramatic impact on supermarkets and are now adjusting their aim on catering outlets. Caterers with little interest in healthy eating could continue to serve relatively unhealthy food with little fear of an immediate effect on sales. However, the growing public interest in healthy food and the trust already placed in caterers give new opportunities for developing the skills of caterers and expanding their role and, lest anyone forget it, their commercial success.

Progressive caterers conduct questionnaires with their customers to learn more about their tastes and interests in health. Some caterers work closely with trades unions in works' canteens, such as at Ford Motors, where strict rules have been laid down on the health component of meals. In the National Health Service, caterers work closely with hospital dietitians to plan healthy meals for patients and staff then visit wards regularly to see how the patients like their work.

Given the share of the nation's nutrition, good and bad, that comes from the industry, it could be said that caterers have a professional responsibility to take account of the health effects of their food. Market trends prove that the popularity of healthy foods goes beyond doctors and nutritionists. Institutions like hospitals and schools, industrial operators like Sutcliffes and Gardner Merchant, and commercial outlets all show positive customer reaction. There is no sign of customer backlash where healthy food is prepared with imagination and skill. On the contrary, they positively welcome the new caring attitude to health.

Along with accepting and developing this new role as a guardian of eaters' health comes increased status for the catering profession. A measure of present status is the caterer's office which can resemble the poky corner of a converted cupboard in the basement. But people tend to respect those professions which help look after their health. Think of nurses, dentists and dietitians. It has already been found, especially in institutional catering within the National Health Service and schools, that caterers taking an interest in healthy food find their local status has improved. With higher status comes more respect and this helps increase the weight of the profession in discussions with management on budgets for better kitchen or dining-room equipment, staff training, and better pay and conditions. More staff satisfaction is likely, which brings lower staff turn-over, better atmosphere in kitchens and perhaps fewer days lost through illness.

The remainder of this section of the book explains why healthy eating is becoming so important and gives clear advice on what healthy diets should be before getting down to the practical matter of turning sound advice into healthy foods in caterers' kitchens.

CHAPTER TWO

HEALTHY EATING: FACTS AND FIGURES

*"One should eat to live, not
live to eat."*
MOLIÈRE, 1622–73

Healthy eating may be fashionable, but it is not new. Molière's popular quote above first appeared over 350 years ago. But literature is also rich in wise words from leading chefs or authorities on 'the culinary art' like Brillat Savarin (1755–1826) who wrote that, 'The destiny of nations depends on the manner wherein they take their food.' Healthy eating is not a modern fad, but its interpretation now is very different from that in Molière's day. Healthy eating is probably more important to the nation's health than ever before.

The science of nutrition, as we now know it, has developed only during the last hundred years. So limited was the understanding of disease and diet in the eighteenth and nineteenth centuries that much of their dietary advice now seems like heresy. Attempts were made to stop an outbreak of cholera in the United States during 1832 by banning the import or sale of fresh fruit which had been judged particularly bad for health. A Dr. Graham, writing in England at the same time, also advised against too many vegetables, especially when raw! Rough and ready experiments had shown that people died on diets without meat, but their conclusion that meat was essential was false because the other diets were often nothing but bread and water, a diet which lacks many vitamins and minerals now known to be necessary for health and life.

Early attempts at scientific studies did however lead to correct conclusions, even though they were not understood at the time. Scurvy was a hazard of long sailing journeys. It produced painful mouth sores which bled and eventually killed sufferers. The effectiveness of citrus fruits in curing scurvy aboard ship was shown by a Scottish naval surgeon in 1747 but he had no idea why it worked. Lime juice became a standard ingredient of ship life and led to the nickname 'Limeys' being given to the English. Early in the nineteenth century it was discovered that cod-liver oil cured that 'English disease' rickets, but again the active ingredient remained a mystery.

It is significant that, even though neither the causes of rickets and scurvy nor the reasons the 'cures' worked were known, both fresh fruit and cod-liver oil became common items in the diets of Europeans specifically to prevent disease. The identification of the missing factors had to wait until early this century when the word 'vitamins' first appeared and the vital nutrients were given letter names A, B, C as they were discovered.

Since the Second World War, medical science has leapt ahead. We now know more about the causes and treatment of disease than ever before in history. But our lifestyle has also changed, perhaps most dramatically in eating habits. While we may be eating more varied diets, and most of us never experience food shortages, there is abundant evidence that our diet is damaging our health.

How ironic. In the affluent countries we are no longer being starved to death but stuffed to death. In abundance, our diet remains a major cause of illness and death. Only the diseases and their causes are different.

Healthy eating is about identifying and correcting those recent dietary changes which are unhealthy.

DIET AND HEALTH

It is shocking, but true, to say that the British are malnourished. 'Mal' means bad; 'bad'-nutrition. There are two important types of malnutrition. First is a shortage of nutrients causing deficiency diseases like rickets, anaemia, beri-beri and scurvy. Second is an excess of nutrients or other components of the diet which lead to diseases like obesity, heart disease, diabetes and cancer, which are common causes of ill health today. By understanding how changes to the diet over time have caused such illness, we are better able to change to healthier diets for the future.

The period from the end of rationing in 1957 until the late 1960s shows a dramatic turn-around in the type of malnutrition common in the UK population. From the eighteenth century to the 1950s, the most common nutritional diseases in Britain were from deficiencies. Before the Second World War, many people's diet consisted of bread, margarine, jam, tea, and fried fish – which was similar to the diet of workers 100 years before – and was short of the vitamin-rich foods like milk, fruit and vegetables which a government committee had said were necessary for health. A famous diet study published in 1936 by John Boyd-Orr showed that only the highest income group, comprising 10 per cent of the population, ate a surplus of all recommended nutrients. The rest were short of more than one vital nutrient, and for many the shortage was both large and constant.

Many nutritionists claim that rationing led to a healthy diet and a healthier British population. There was a fall in the amount of fats, sugar and meat eaten, and an increase in bread, potatoes and milk available. The ration was calculated to meet what were known then to be nutritional needs. By concentrating on foods which could be grown in Britain, the war-time diet had the same protein as before, a healthy reduction in energy (or calories) but more of the valuable vitamins and minerals than many were eating before the war. Rationing not only ensured everybody had equal access to foods, it also subsidised the prices. This meant the poor ate a more nutritious diet and the more affluent at least maintained their nutrition.

Table 1 shows the broad changes to some categories of food available in the UK from the pre-war period to the present. Note the fall in amounts of beef, lamb and fish compared to the rapid rise in poultry. Total meat consumption has not changed much since 1955, but there has been a shift to more poultry, sausages and other cheap meat products. Fresh fish consumption has fallen, largely because consumers do not like the smell and the need to clean fish, especially when there are more vacuum packs of meat and neatly dressed frozen chickens readily available. From 1980, margarine has pushed butter into second place but the total amount of yellow fat eaten has fallen only slightly. The fall in flour reflects a general drop in the amounts of all carbohydrate foods eaten as well as a decline in home baking. There has been a steady loss of interest in potatoes but the figure is for all potatoes entering the food chain. Looked at more closely, there has been a large fall in potatoes eaten as a vegetable with increasing amounts going into crisps, frozen oven-ready chips and dehydrated products. Fresh fruit has not changed much over 40 years despite the greater variety of home-grown and exotic types in the shops. Canned fruit in syrups are losing out to fresh and frozen fruit, but the biggest change has been in the drinking of fruit juices.

These changes were fuelled by a mixture of economic prosperity, improving technology in agriculture and the rapid growth of a new food manufacturing industry. From the early 1950s more and more foods were processed or manufactured so that shops filled with boxes, packets, cans and bottles of food products. Not only did the mixture of foods eaten change as Table 1 shows, but the composition of food changed. Over three quarters of all food eaten today is processed at least once, much of it several times. In manufacturing, traditional foods – meat, flour, potatoes – become raw materials which are combined with fats and sugars to make new products which are textured, flavoured, coloured and preserved with 'additives'. While the variety of foods has increased, many are made of refined ingredients and the valuable nutrition in the original food ingredients is

Table 1 Changing food supplies in the UK (kg food per head per year)

Food	Pre-war	1947	1955	1965	1975	1985
Dairy (− butter)	17.4	22.0	23.9	25.1	26.4	25.8
Beef (bone in)	24.1	14.6	20.3	17.9	21.3	19.0
Mutton and lamb	11.4	11.0	11.1	10.5	8.3	6.9
Poultry	2.3	2.2	2.9	7.6	11.4	16.0
Fish (fresh and frozen)	9.9	12.9	8.6	7.8	6.1	5.3
Eggs (total no.)	220	191	229	271	246	224
Butter	11.2	5.1	6.7	8.8	8.4	5.0
Margarine	3.9	6.8	8.0	4.4	4.3	7.3
Sugar	41.2	35.7	46.2	45.4	38.9	37.3
Potatoes	86.2	129.7	106.2	100.9	101.7	107.6
Cabbage	21.1	23.3	17.0	17.0	15.0	15.9
Carrots	4.0	6.0	5.2	5.5	5.0	8.5
Fruit (fresh)	35.6	30.9	30.1	33.4	31.5	36.3
Fruit (canned)	4.7	2.0	6.3	8.6	6.8	4.8
Flour	88.2	102.0	82.8	70.3	64.4	58.7
Breakfast cereals	0.8	1.4	1.9	2.4	3.5	3.9

Sources: Economic Trends (1978); *Statistical Information*, 12 October 1987, MAFF.

often lost or diluted. These changes have meant that the composition of the diet has changed in an unhealthy direction.

There is less dietary fibre than before, as well as less energy coming from starchy carbohydrates and more from fats. Much of this fat is saturated which is believed to be one of the most important causes of heart disease and many cancers. With well over 3,000 foods available in supermarkets now it is difficult to imagine how changes to these foods has affected the overall diet. But when the whole diet is analysed into the basic components, a steady change in composition can be seen clearly from the end of rationing (Figure 1, p. 16).

The total amount of protein eaten has remained remarkably steady but more of it now comes from animal than vegetable sources. The top line of the graph shows that the amount of energy eaten each day has fallen. This is partly because there is less physical activity at work, getting to and from work, or at play, but also because with better home heating less energy is needed just to keep warm. Even so many people still eat too much energy and the Royal College of Physicians says that about 1 in 5 Britons are overweight.

The amount of fat eaten has fallen slightly over the period, but the most important measure of fat in the diet is its contribution to the total energy content of the diet. The graph shows that the percentage of energy from fat has increased by nearly 20 per cent in forty years and by 1985 was the highest ever recorded at 42.4 per cent of energy. Since 1955 there has been

Changes in the percentage contribution of fat, protein and carbohydrate to total per caput dietary energy supply.

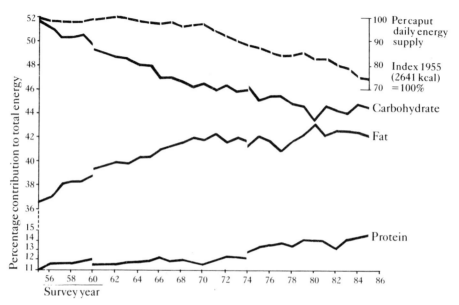

Note: The breaks at 1960 and 1974 are due to revised conversion factors

Source: MAFF Household Food Consumption and Expenditure, various years

a fall in the amount of animal (both meat and dairy) fat but more vegetable fats and oils have been eaten as margarines and cooking oils. But because many vegetable oils have been hardened in manufacturing, which makes them more saturated than the original oil, there has been little change in the chemical composition of the fats eaten – nearly half of the fat in the diet is saturated. (Saturated fats are explained on pp. 25–27.)

As the percentage of dietary energy from fat increased, that from total carbohydrates fell. These are mainly derived from starch in root vegetables, cereals and pulses, but sugar is also a carbohydrate and is replacing starch in the total amount of carbohydrates eaten. It should come as no surprise that dietary fibre has fallen as less carbohydrate is eaten since fibre comes entirely from cereals, fruits and vegetables.

These dietary changes have been shown either to cause or to be strongly associated with some of the most common diseases now affecting the UK population:

disease	dietary cause
obesity and overweight	excess energy (calories)
tooth decay	sugar
heart attack	fat, cholesterol, salt
stroke	salt
high blood pressure	salt
diverticular disease	
constipation	
irritable colon	insufficient dietary fibre
appendicitis	
cancer of large bowel and colon	insufficient dietary fibre, too much fat
breast cancer	fat
gallstones	fat, cholesterol
diabetes	fat, sugar, insufficient fibre

Things are not quite as simple as the list suggests. Only the major dietary causes are listed. Many of these diseases are complex in their causes and often there are more factors involved, including some of the minor nutrients in some diseases. It has been found, for example, that people with low amounts of carotene or Vitamin C in their diets may be more likely to have certain cancers, and that people eating diets with low amounts of a special type of fat called essential fatty acids or EFAs are more likely to have heart disease if they also have too much saturated fat in the diet.

Not all diet-related diseases are fatal, but even those which aren't cause unnecessary suffering, loss of work and National Health Service expenditure. Most of us are born healthy and want to stay that way. Doctors and nutritionists have learned that simple corrections to the diet can help us avoid or at least reduce the severity of these diseases and stay healthy.

It can't be emphasised enough that the strength of the scientific evidence is sufficient for action to be taken at a national level. All the health professional organisations like the British Dietetic Association and the Royal College of Physicians make official statements in support of healthy eating. This is not the place to be outlining the evidence, but it is impressive that the UK government has been advising since 1978 that the whole population change its diet. Governments in all other industrialised countries also make similar recommendations. The UK government is convinced – the minister of agriculture has stated publicly that so strong is the evidence that fat is a cause of heart disease, he wants EEC food labelling laws changed to allow the UK to have compulsory fat labelling on foods so consumers can follow advice to eat less fat to protect their hearts.

Almost without exception, people who say there is not enough evidence are either the food industries' public relations representatives, or medical consultants paid by the industry. Check the origin of advertisements in trade journals or in mailings landing on unsuspecting caterers' desks. The advice described below is that supported by the government's Health Education Authority and follows the leading independent medical organisations in the UK. Don't let yourself be confused by unqualified doubters or vested interests who may not want you to make the change – when in doubt ask your local Health Authority dietitian.

A HEALTHY DIET

Just as our national diet has changed, so the definition of a healthy diet must be brought into line. The old wisdom of a 'balanced' diet being a necessary mixture of foods to provide the minimum of nutrients is no longer enough. A 'balanced diet or meal' was meant to contain a variety of foods including meats and dairy foods to give 'proteins for growth', fruits and vegetables to supply 'protective minerals and vitamins'. A glance at the list of diet-related diseases above shows that none is caused primarily by deficiencies of protein, minerals or vitamins. The national diet has greater variety than ever before and major deficiency diseases are now rare. The minerals and vitamins do still matter to health, however, and there are good reasons to keep them under surveillance. For example, recent diet surveys still show that some people's intakes of folic acid or iron are low enough to cause concern.

The NACNE (National Advisory Committee on Nutrition Education) report published in 1983 is the most important document on dietary advice to be published in the UK this century. It described the scientific evidence relating the composition of the diet to specific diseases and also gave for the first time clear recommendations on how to change the national diet in a more healthy direction. NACNE recognised that proteins, minerals and vitamins were important for health but concluded that the present diet had sufficient amounts of nearly all of these nutrients for health, except for groups with special needs like pregnant women, the sick and the elderly for whom special dietary care is always advisable. The NACNE Committee focused on the more important need to shift the overall composition of the national diet back towards that which existed in the UK about 1950 (see Figure 1, p. 16).

The NACNE healthy diet recommendation is:

● Energy (calorie) intake should be enough to maintain optimum body weight and adequate exercise.

- Total fat eaten should be no more than 30 per cent of total energy eaten.

- Saturated fatty acids should be no more than 10 per cent of total energy.

- Sugar eaten should be reduced, on average, to not more than 20 kg per person a year with not more than 10 kg per person from snack foods.

- Dietary fibre should be increased from an average of 20 g to 30 g per person per day.

- Salt should fall by about 3 g per person a day.

- Alcohol should be reduced from an average of about 7 per cent of energy intake to no more than 4 per cent.

The NACNE advice should be followed by all the population. There is no point in arguing that only those people at risk of diseases like high blood pressure, strokes, heart attacks or cancers need bother to change. The truth is that there is no useful way of telling who will get the disease until it appears. The dietary factors are called risk factors because they *increase your chances of getting one or more of the diseases*. The more risk factors, and the more of any single risk factor, the higher the chances of disease. The message therefore is straightforward: the fewer dietary risk factors the healthier we will stay. This means that all healthy people have good reasons to follow healthy eating. People already at high risk also have reason to correct their diet. It is never too late.

The recommendations are very useful because they allow caterers and other diet planners to compare the compositions of present meals and diets with these guidelines which show what has to be changed and by how much to make the diet healthy. NACNE has become accepted as the most useful statement of the general principles of healthy eating and of the quantities of different constituents to aim for. Most National Health Authorities use NACNE and its advice forms the starting point for most government and other organisations' dietary advice. There may be some variation in the amounts of each diet constituent recommended for health or the time over which any changes should occur, but the same general direction and degree of change is common to all this advice.

When applied to the average diet in the UK, the NACNE guidelines mean that:

Total fat should be **cut by a quarter**
Saturated fat **cut by half**
Sugar **cut by half**
Dietary fibre **up by half**
Salt **cut by a quarter**

Note carefully the important advice about fats. Saturated fat is to be cut by **half**, whereas total fat is to be cut by only a **quarter**. This is very often overlooked. Too many interpretations of NACNE say only that total fat should be reduced. NACNE recognises that the saturated fats are the main culprits in causing heart disease and possibly certain cancers. This presents no problems for caterers though because, as is shown on pp. 25–27, saturated fats are easily identified and are easy to reduce.

COMA PANEL ADVICE

In 1984, the Department of Health's COMA Panel (Committee on Medical Aspects of Food Policy) published its second report on diet and heart disease. COMA also made strong recommendations that total fat and *especially saturated fat* should be reduced to help prevent heart disease. They accepted the NACNE guidelines for people at high risk but proposed a slightly lower reduction *for immediate action*. The NACNE guidelines also proposed a slightly lower degree of change for implementation before the end of the 1980s and these are very close to those of the COMA Panel (Table 2). COMA also accepted that there should be no further increase in sugars, that a reduction in salt would be beneficial and that fibre-rich carbohydrates should replace some of the energy lost from the diet when fat is reduced.

There is no disagreement between the two reports. COMA was looking at the relationships between diet and heart disease alone, whereas NACNE was concerned with all diseases. COMA did not recommend a specific cut in sugar because there is no strong evidence that sugar is a direct cause of heart disease. However, COMA did accept that there were other health reasons for reducing sugar which can be read as a reference to the earlier NACNE advice.

Table 2 Advice on dietary fats as percentage of total energy

Dietary component	NACNE long term	NACNE 1980s	COMA immediate
Total fat	30	34	35
Saturated fat	10	15	15
P:S ratio	–	to .32	to .45

Note: the P:S ratio is the amount of polyunsaturated fatty acids divided by the amount of saturated fatty acids in a fat or oil and gives a simple measure of their relative proportions. A P:S ratio less than 1 means there are more saturated fatty acids than polyunsaturated types in a fat. A ratio greater than 1 means there are more polyunsaturated fatty acids than saturated which is the better proportion for health.

COMA offered specific recommendations to caterers as important professionals with opportunities to help the public eat more healthily. It was suggested that, 'Where appropriate, foods or food products with lower contents of saturated plus trans fatty acids and/or common salt than is at present customary should be made available to the general public.' Also, caterers were asked to provide more information about the fat content of their foods to help customers make choices.

Throughout this book the NACNE guidelines are used when talking about healthy diets because they recommend the dietary mix which the population should be aiming to reach over the coming 5 to 10 years. Many changes towards healthy catering can be made immediately, but others, like caterer training and the availability of healthy commodities, will take longer. We should see NACNE as the ultimate goal and work towards it. Chapter 4 shows how the NACNE healthy diet advice can be used in choosing healthy ingredients, designing healthy recipes and providing healthy meals and diets for customers.

MINERALS AND VITAMINS

It is striking that the NACNE guidelines do not give specific recommendations for the amounts of minerals and vitamins in a healthy diet. This emphasises how the most important diet-related diseases have moved away from the deficiency diseases of the 1950s and earlier. But an adequate supply of vitamins and minerals are still essential for good health. Although most people's diets include sufficient because of the greater quantity and variety of nutritious foods now eaten (see Table 3, p. 29), the combination of low incomes and a narrow choice of foods from our highly processed food supply can easily lead to a shortage in some people's diets.

Minerals and vitamins in food are invisible. So all caterers need to be aware of the food sources of these nutrients and how food preparation, cooking and serving affect the amounts in the food on the table. Some caterers, especially those in institutions like hospitals, residential homes for the elderly or chronically ill, or the armed services and prisons, however, need to pay special attention to vitamins and minerals. For example, analysis of food in a geriatric hospital in the London Borough of Brent during 1983 found that these long-stay patients were having less than half the amount of vitamin C recommended for the general population. Low levels of this vitamin are common in institutional catering. This case was serious as vitamin C deficiency delays the healing of injuries and wounds after operations, and is believed to be one cause of depression in elderly people. The caterer and dietitian found a simple and popular solution – a glass of orange juice each day.

The more of the customers' daily food that is supplied by caterers, the more important that food is to the customers' vitamin and mineral needs. There are at least 15 minerals and 13 vitamins needed for health:

Minerals	Trace elements	Vitamins
calcium	chromium	vitamin A
iron	cobalt	thiamine (B$_1$)
magnesium	copper	riboflavin (B$_2$)
phosphorus	fluorine	nicotinic acid
potassium	iodine	vitamin B$_6$
sodium	manganese	vitamin B$_{12}$
	selenium	folic acid
	zinc	pantothenic acid
		biotin
		vitamin C
		vitamin D
		vitamin E
		vitamin K

Appendix I gives a summary of the nutritional function of each mineral and vitamin and lists important food sources.

A guide to how much of each mineral and vitamin is needed for health is contained in tables of Recommended Daily Amounts (RDA), or sometimes called the Recommended Daily Allowances or even Recommended Daily Intakes (RDI). Unlike the NACNE guidelines which suggest *maximum* amounts for health of parts of the diet, the RDAs show the *minimum* amounts necessary for health. To eat more than the RDA is better so long as the amounts do not reach toxic levels, which is possible with vitamins A, B and D.

Appendix III gives the current RDAs for the UK as published by the Department of Health and Social Security (DHSS), now called the Department of Health (DOH). The RDAs are useful for caterers but are so often misunderstood that it is helpful to take careful note of the following:

● The RDAs are meant to be used for healthy people only. The ill, eldery, or people with special dietary needs may require additional advice which is best provided by a doctor or dietitian.

• The RDAs do not give the nutrient needs for each individual. They are meant to be an average minimum intake to ensure that nearly every person in the population will have sufficient nutrients. The RDA for each nutrient is calculated by taking data from scientific studies to find the amount needed to ensure that no person in a large group of people will show any deficiency symptoms and then multiplying that amount by 2 or 3 times to give a large margin of safety. Notice also that there are different needs for men and women, for young and old, different levels of physical activity, and for pregnant or breastfeeding women.

• Individual needs vary greatly. There is no easy, or even useful way of discovering each person's individual need for each nutrient. But that is not important because, so long as the RDAs are there on the plate and eaten, there is almost no chance that any person will be short of an essential nutrient. At the same time, people who need smaller than average amounts will have much more than they need but will come to no harm.

• Notice that the RDA table includes only 10 nutrients apart from energy. This does not mean that other nutrients are not important. The DHSS list includes all nutrients for which a useful RDA has been worked out. Others may be added as the RDAs are revised.

• Despite all the precise-looking numbers in the table of RDAs, it is a mistake to treat them as measures of *exact needs*. Nutritionists know that many of the original scientific studies do not give clear enough data for *exact* measures and some of the RDAs are more like learned guesses. The UK figure for protein, for example, is about double that of many other countries and the reason is simple and quaint. Here, the RDA for protein is set at 10 per cent of the RDA for energy for the simple reason that that is how much protein is eaten in the UK. This is why many nutritionists, even in the DHSS, say 'it would do no harm for most people to eat a little less protein'. So remember the RDAs are a guide only.

• The RDAs are very useful in analysing recipes, cooking methods, menus and longer-term diets. Existing menus or diets can be analysed to see how they provide basic nutrients and when planning new healthy menus and recipes the overall nutritional content can be checked during development and testing.

PROTEINS

There is much confusion about protein which can lead to unnecessary expense in catering.

Protein deficiency is almost unheard-of in Britain today. The amount eaten on average has not changed for 50 years even though the proportion of meat protein has increased to about 60 per cent of the total with only 30 per cent now coming from vegetable protein. Young, active children need more protein for each kg of body weight than older, less active adults but they still don't need 'protein-rich' meals. Young children also need more energy for their weight than adults and so long as about 10 per cent of the total energy is protein, they will have enough protein – the more energy they use, the more protein in their diet.

Eating more protein than the body needs will not mean more muscles or even better health. Excess protein, like excess fat or carbohydrate will be stored as fat.

There is no need to worry about different qualities of protein unless the amount in the diet is close to the minimum needed. Proteins are made up of different chemicals called amino acids. There are about twenty different amino acids and the different types of protein in plants or animals have different mixtures of these amino acids. Eight amino acids are essential in human diets as they cannot be made in the body. Meat and other animal foods like eggs are high in all the essential amino acids and are therefore called 'high biological quality' proteins. Most plant proteins have relatively low amounts of one or more essential amino acids and thus have a lower biological value or quality. Cereals tend to have only small amounts of lysine or tryptophan and legumes (or pulses) are low in methionine. However, since diets normally have a mixture of proteins and the amount of protein eaten is nearly double the daily needs (Table 3), there is little chance of running short of an essential amino acid.

Meat is an expensive protein and there is no reason why human protein needs must come from meats, or even eggs and dairy products despite their convenience. (Vegetarians despair with the frequency of omelettes and cheese being the only 'vegetarian alternatives' on menus.) Mixtures of cereals and pulses are quite adequate suppliers of dietary proteins as the health of vegetarians and vegans shows. Caterers who reduce the amount of meat in dishes, or the number of meat dishes on menus, can save on budgets without any fear of harming their customers' nutrition. If worried about the adequacy of protein in low-meat or vegetarian meals, a useful guiding rule is 'beans with everything' which will help ensure a suitable mixture of types of proteins in the meal. But please do not read 'baked beans' for 'beans'! Only a dull caterer need fear harming the customer's enjoyment through eating less meat.

FATS

There are fats and fats and plenty of confusion in between. It is important to be clear about the essentials. A short summary is as follows.

Fats and oils are the same type of chemical, loosely called fat. Fats tend to be solid at room temperature and oils are liquid. Once heated during cooking, all fats become liquid.

Terms like *saturated* and *polyunsaturated* are sources of great confusion but this is easily resolved. There are three main uses of the terms.

- *Composition of fats and oils.* Both are made up of chemicals called triglycerides and each triglyceride consists of a unit of glycerol to which is attached three chemicals called fatty acids. The fatty acids decide the type of fat. Like the amino acids in proteins, there are about twenty-five different fatty acids. Some can be made in the body but others must be eaten in food and are called 'essential fatty acids' or EFAs.

The fatty acids are chains of carbon atoms between 10 and 22 atoms in length. All along the chains are hydrogen atoms attached to the carbons by single bonds. The carbons are joined together like beads which clip together making a necklace. Most have only a single clip or bond between them, but some fatty acids have a number of carbons joined by double clips or bonds. Carbons with double bonds are chemically reactive and the number of these double bonds says whether the fatty acid is saturated (no double bonds), monounsaturated (only one double bond) or polyunsaturated (between 2 and 6 double bonds) – see Figure 2.

That is the complicated bit – because different fats and oils have different combinations of fatty acids, whether they are saturated or not depends on the mixture of their fatty acids. A saturated fat – like butter, lard, coconut oil – is mostly saturated fatty acids like palmitic. Monounsaturated fats like olive oil contain mostly oleic fatty acid which has one double bond. Polyunsaturated fats – maize, soya, fish oils – have large proportions of fatty acids with two or more double bonds.

Diagrammatic view of different degrees of saturation in fatty acids

saturated   ●-●-●-●-●-●-●-●-●-●-●-●-●-●-●-●-●-●   stearic acid
                                                      18 carbon atoms
                                                      no double bond

mono-unsaturated   ●-●-●-●-●-●-●-●=●-●-●-●-●-●-●-●-●-●   oleic acid
                                                      18 carbon atoms
                                                      1 double bond

poly-unsaturated   ●-●-●=●-●-●=●-●-●=●-●-●-●-●-●-●-●-●   ∝-linolenic acid
                                                      18 carbon atoms
                                                      3 double bonds

● *Fats and health*. Contrary to common belief, only a small amount of fat is necessary for health – about 10 per cent of total energy need be fat. The only fats needed are polyunsaturated fats or EFAs. No saturated fat is necessary for health.

Fats are a useful source of energy, and some fats carry with them valuable vitamins like A and D.

Saturated fats have been identified as one cause of heart disease and even of some cancers. Too much of any kind of fat will help encourage overweight or obesity. There is increasing evidence that polyunsaturated fats may protect against heart disease and that one group of the EFAs known as the 'omega-3' series are particularly beneficial. 'Omega-3' fats are found in plant oils like soya and linseed, and also in fish oils, but there is no need to take them as diet supplements.

● *Which fat to use?* Most dietary fat comes from visible sources – dairy fat, cooking fat and oils, salad oils, margarines and low-fat spreads. This makes it easy to make healthy choices. Because of the effects of manufacturing and processing on fats, it is not enough to say that animal fats are saturated while plant oils and fats are unsaturated. Dairy fats in butter, cheese and milk are highly saturated and should be a prime target for reduction; lard and dripping should be avoided as very saturated but there are plenty of good substitutes. Among the cooking and salad oils avoid coconut and palm which are saturated and go for soya, maize (or corn), sunflower, olive, rape (or colza) oils most of which are high in polyunsaturates and all of which are low in unhealthy saturates. Choose products with the type of plant oil named. Margarines and spreads are more difficult because it is impossible to tell how much of the original polyunsaturated fats have been destroyed during the process of 'hydrogenation' to harden the fats in manufacture. Also many spreads contain mixtures of plant and animal (or fish) fats which are not specified on all labels. Many of these foods now give a nutrition label which lists the composition of fats, but catering packs usually do not. Appendix II lists the fat content and type of fat in common margarines.

Cholesterol is another form of fat found in animal and sea foods. Too much in the diet can help cause heart disease but it is now thought that the saturated fat in the diet has a greater effect in pushing up the surplus cholesterol in the blood which damages the arteries and heart. Still some foods – egg yolks, offal meats, shell fish – are very rich in cholesterol and it is best to eat these foods less often.

DIETARY FIBRE

Fibre is found only in plant foods but is much more than wheat bran. Fibre is plant cell walls as well as substances like gums and pectin which are very different from the 'roughage' idea of bran but are parts of plants. Some foods are rich in fibre – whole cereals, all pulses, root vegetables, fruits like apples and pears, and dried fruits, especially figs, apricots and prunes.

CARBOHYDRATES

There is often confusion about carbohydrates which gives them a bad reputation among caterers and their customers.

Carbohydrates are common in both plant and animal cells. Their basic role is as a means of storing energy and of moving it about from cell to cell where it may be stored or needed as 'fuel' for cells or organs to function. There are two main types of carbohydrate of interest in diets – sugars and starch.

Sugars include milk sugar (or lactose), fructose, glucose and sucrose which is common white sugar. Starches are long chains of simple sugars joined together. They have different properties from the free sugars, the most obvious difference being that they are not soluble in cold water, which is useful to the plants where they are used to store energy. Plant leaves convert the sun's energy to sugars which are soluble and can be moved around the plant to where they are needed or to be stored. Sugars are converted to starch in potato tubers, wheat grains, maize, etc. When needed, starch is converted back into sugars which are an easily used source of energy in plant cells.

Once eaten by humans, starches are broken down into free sugar molecules and are digested and used in the same way as any sugars that are eaten. Weight for weight, starch and sugar have the same calories (energy) but there are important differences which affect how much of each should be eaten. Sugars are sweet and this encourages more to be eaten than the appetite might suggest, which is why they can contribute to overweight. Sugars, especially when eaten in sticky foods like sweets and cakes, cause more dental caries than starchy foods like potato, rice or bread.

Carbohydrates are not essential in a healthy diet in the same way that proteins or vitamins are, but they are a very useful source of energy. Unrefined starchy foods like root vegetables, wholemeal bread, and whole cereals in all forms are the best ways of eating carbohydrates. Refined forms like white sugar, sweets or white flour are not the best ways of eating carbohydrates. Why eat energy alone when foods with the energy plus other nutrients like minerals and vitamins or with fibre are available? Refined carbohydrates give only energy.

Weight for weight, fat has twice the calories of carbohydrates. Any reduction in total energy in the diet from cutting down on unhealthy fats should be made up with an increase in starchy carbohydrate foods. Starchy carbohydrate foods are not fattening unless they are eaten with calorie-rich fats or refined sugars.

WHAT IS THE BRITISH DIET?

There is no one British diet. Even if it could be identified, everyone knows that their own diet changes each day and that no two days are the same. But there are identifiable features of British eating – bacon and eggs, white sliced bread, kippers, bangers and pease pudding, etc. It is also possible to record the types and amounts of all food eaten by a proportion of the population and, by dividing by the number of people involved, calculate an 'average diet'. This is done for the whole country by the National Food Survey (NFS) which is a weekly survey throughout the whole year (except for Christmas week) of about 7,000 households selected from electoral registers throughout Britain.

Over a week, one person in each household records everything bought to eat at home together with the number of adults and children (including guests) eating each meal. From these week-long diaries are calculated both how much of each food is brought home to eat and its nutritional composition. This data is very useful as a picture of the 'average diet'. The survey is continual and gives an accurate measure of changes in eating habits and hence indications of nutritional problems and improvements. Look at Table 1 (p. 15), and Table 3 below which shows how the nutritional content of the national average diet compares with the RDAs.

The NFS data is broken down into different regions of the country, household sizes, and incomes of households so it presents a number of 'average' or typical diets for different social and economic groups across the country. This data is helpful to caterers in different parts of Britain where eating patterns are different. The nutritional importance of different foods can change with the diet. Scotland has the lowest consumption of fruit and vegetables with the South West the highest, with each person eating three quarters of a kilogram more a week than the Scots. Londoners eat least sugar, with the West Midlands topping the list with nearly 30 per cent more sugar than Londoners. The North of England generally eats much less cheese than the Midlands and South East.

There is a difference between the amounts of fat or vitamin C which

Table 3 Nutritional quality of the national average diet (1986)

Nutrient		Consumption per person per day	% of RDA
Energy	k cal	2070	93
	MJ	8.7	93
Total protein	g	69.3	168
Animal protein	g	42.9	
Fat (total)	g	98	NA
Fatty acids			
Saturated	g	40.6	NA
Mono	g	35.8	NA
Polyunsaturates	g	11.3	NA
Carbohydrate	g	244	NA
Calcium	mg	890	163
Iron	mg	11.3	105
Thiamine	mg	1.39	151
Riboflavin	mg	1.82	132
Niacin equivalent	mg	28	179
Vitamin C	mg	60	206
Vitamin A equivalent	µg	1330	190
Vitamin D	µg	3.24	NA

NA = not applicable.
Source: MAFF, *Household Food Consumption and Expenditure, 1986*, London, HMSO, 1987.

should be in a diet and picturing how these nutrients occur in the foods and the diets which people eat. The NFS data helps by providing information on how the foods in the average diet contribute to the total intake of each nutrient. This information is essential for caterers to know how to change the diet to make it healthier. For example, it is well known that liver is one of the richest food sources of iron but it may not be the best way of increasing the amount of iron eaten by customers. Why? The NFS data in Table 4 show that only 1.8 per cent of all the iron in the average diet comes from liver for the simple, and obvious, reason that most people eat liver infrequently and then in small amounts. Even were all people to eat twice as much liver at a sitting or to eat it twice as often, the contribution of liver to the total amount of iron in the diet would still remain below 5 per cent. There are better ways of increasing iron intake. Table 4 also shows that liquid milk and cheese together supply as much saturated fat as all meat eaten which suggests that encouraging the use of more skimmed, or even semi-skimmed milk, would be a very useful way of reducing the saturated fats as recommended by NACNE.

The contributions made by the major foods in the British diet to intakes of fat, energy and vitamins and minerals are listed in detail in Appendix IV which comes from the NFS data. It shows how to value different foods according to their contribution to the diet which is as important as their nutrient content. The importance of this will become more clear when recipe modification and menu planning are considered.

Table 4 Contributions of different foods to saturated fat and iron in average diets, NFS, 1986

Food group	% sat. fat supplied	% total iron supplied
Liquid milk, cream, cheese	25.8	2.4
Total meat	24.3	18.2
Liver	.1	1.8
Total fish	.8	1.9
Butter	11.9	.1
Margarine	9.9	.5
Other fats and oils	10.5	.1
Total vegetables	1.7	16.7
Total fruit	.7	4.1
Total cereals (inc. bread, biscuits, cakes etc.)	10.5	45.0
Other foods	3.8	9.2
	100 (40.6 g)	100 (11.3 g)

Source: MAFF data drawn from NFS, 1986.

The NFS does not include food eaten out of the home so all catering meals are excluded. There is no similar survey of catering foods eaten, but there are frequent market research surveys of different sectors of the catering industry. These give a rough picture of the nutritional content of meals eaten out of the home but it is not good news. Catering meals, take-aways and snacks are different foods from those prepared at home and they have a different composition. Catering foods as a whole tend to be more fatty, more sugary, and use more manufactured and refined foods than those eaten at home, suggesting the scope for healthy catering.

SPECIAL DIETARY NEEDS

Some medical conditions require special diets – diabetes, coeliac disease, food intolerances. But there are also diets which people choose to follow for religious, cultural or ethical reasons. Caterers need to be aware of the requirements of these diets and to pay scrupulous attention to the rules. Avoid any temptation to break rules that seem of little importance or which the caterer may feel will not be noticed. Customers' health could be threatened. The smallest trace of beef stock in food will be a serious breach to any Hindu and most vegetarians, many of whom are able to detect by taste any such indiscretions. A customer on a gluten-free diet could be made quite ill if a small amount of wheat flour was in their food. Strict adherence to all rules will bring both satisfied and trusting customers. Customers who are unsure of the contents of their food may reject all offers and explanations rather than risk a breach of their own dietary rules.

Although these diets are distinguished by their restrictions, it is a mistake to see them as either difficult to handle in the kitchen or necessarily unacceptable to customers who don't follow such a diet.

VEGETARIANS

Vegetarians are the best known group with a special diet. It has been estimated that there are 4.3 million adults and children in the UK who claim to be vegetarian. Only about half of these are strict vegetarians with the remainder at least avoiding red meats but possibly eating fish or cheese made with animal rennet.

Vegetarian rules. Strict vegetarians do not eat meat, poultry, fish, or any products from slaughter houses. Dairy products may be eaten but not cheese made with rennet which is an enzyme taken from the stomach of calves. Eggs are usually eaten, but should be free-range.

Beware of ingredients containing animal products. Gelatin should be avoided as it is made from animal bones and tissue but this is not made clear on packaging. This means avoiding aspic, and not using either block or jelly crystals for glazing, moulding or any other use. Gelatin is added to set some yoghurts. Check cooking oils and fats to make sure there are no animal fats as ingredients – avoid lard, dripping, tallow, suet and fish oils. A common problem is using frying fats or oils to cook vegetarian food after first frying animal foods – don't. Watch flavourings like Worcestershire-type sauces which often contain items like anchovies. Animal fats may be added to breads but this can be checked with bakeries. Be very wary about packet mixes which often have animal ingredients.

Caterers' suppliers now have a wide range of alternatives for ingredients rejected by vegetarians:

UNACCEPTABLE	ALTERNATIVE
MEAT, FISH, POULTRY	*Cereals, pulses, nuts, seeds (sunflower, pumpkin), eggs, root and other vegetables, TVP, tofu, seitan*
MEAT, FISH STOCKS	*Vegetable stocks, yeast extracts, vegetable stock cubes*
ANIMAL FATS AND FISH OILS	*Trex, Pura, 100% vegetable oils and margarines, vegetarian suet, Nutter*
BATTERY EGGS	*Free-range eggs*
GELATIN, ASPIC, JELLY FOR GLAZING	*Agar agar, Gelozone, apple pectin*
ANIMAL-FAT ICE-CREAM	*Vegetable-fat types*
ANIMAL-BASED FLAVOURINGS	*Yeast extracts, soya sauce, miso, herbs and spices, Holbrook's Worcester sauce (which is anchovy-free), Vecon*
CHEESE MADE WITH ANIMAL RENNET	*Special vegetarian cheese, most cottage cheese, some curd cheese*

Vegans exclude all animal products from their diet. In addition to the restrictions of vegetarians, they also avoid all milk, milk products and eggs. Vegan diets must be more carefully controlled than vegetarian to ensure adequate amounts of essential nutrients. The most common deficient nutrients are iron, riboflavin and vitamin B_{12}. Mixtures of cereal, pulses and nuts as the basis of vegan meals help ensure good protein supply together with other nutrients. Yeast extracts are a good source of the important B vitamins and many vegan foods have additional supplements. Despite the risk of some vitamins which are most concentrated in animal products being in short supply, vegan diets are very healthy since they have a large amount of fruits and vegetables, increasing fibre, minerals and most vitamins, but are low in saturated animal fats.

In addition to the suggested alternatives for vegetarians above, the following apply to vegans:

UNACCEPTABLE	ALTERNATIVE
MEAT, EGG, CHEESE DISHES	*Cereals, pulses, nuts*
MILK	*Soya and cereal-based milks; soya curds and TVP are useful for vegans but make sure they contain no animal ingredients*
CREAM	*Excellent alternative made with cashew nuts blended with water*
BUTTER, MARGARINE	*Many vegetable margarines contain whey, milk solids, but suitable brands are available e.g. Vitaquel, Tomor*
HONEY IS OFTEN AVOIDED	*Sugar or jams depending on use of the honey*

Diets for ethnic minorities are most likely to interest institutional caterers but both commercial and industrial caterers also have demands for these special dietary needs. The most widespread ethnic or religious dietary needs in the UK are:

HINDUS

Most Hindus are vegetarians and many, especially women, avoid eggs. The cow is sacred and even Hindus who are not vegetarians will not eat any beef. However lamb, chicken and pork may be eaten along with white, firm fish.

Staple foods are cereals baked as chapatis and other breads, rice with pulses, milk, yoghurt and home-made cheeses supplying the protein base. Butter or vegetable-oil 'ghee' is used for frying but lard, dripping and other animal carcase-derived fats are strictly avoided.

MUSLIMS

Meat can be eaten with the strict exception of pig and meats from any carnivorous animals. Meat must be slaughtered according to Islamic laws and is known as Halal meat. Fish, eggs and dairy foods are allowed. Lard (made from pig fat) is forbidden and Muslims will also avoid foods like cakes, pastries, ice-cream and margarines which contain, or are thought to contain, lard or fat from animals not killed in the correct Islamic way. Thus it is best to avoid all animal fats in cooking, whether for frying or as ingredients. Alcohol is also strictly forbidden, even as an ingredient.

JUDAISM

The degree of adherence to the Jewish food laws (Laws of Kashrut) varies but the basic rules should be known and discussed with customers as necessary. Strict adherence presents some difficulties because of the need to keep foods and utensils completely separate rather than only avoid certain ingredients. The Laws of Kashrut mean that:

● Only meat from animals with a cloven hoof and which chew cud are permitted – sheep, beef, goat, deer but not pigs or rabbits.

● Meat must be killed by Jewish slaughter methods.

● Only herbivorous birds may be eaten – chicken, turkey, duck, goose, pheasant, partridge, pigeon and dove.

● Only fish with fins and scales are allowed and all shellfish, squid, octopus forbidden.

● Meat and milk foods must be kept apart in cooking and eating.

Strict kosher Jews may not eat in any catering establishment unless it has been approved by a Rabbi. It pays to check with a local synagogue.

MEDICAL MODIFICATIONS OF DIETS

These should always be checked with a dietitian as well as the customer. Each District Health Authority has dietitians who can advise on medical and other special diets as well as recommend supportive literature for caterers. The Department of Health has a Catering Branch which publishes information for caterers and many of the special patient-care organisations like the Coeliac and Diabetic Societies also provide advisory services to caterers. Appendix V has a list of relevant addresses.

CHAPTER THREE

THE HEALTHY CATERER: PUTTING THEORY TO WORK

> *"The Creator, though*
> *condemning man to eat to*
> *live, invites him to do so by*
> *appetite, and rewards him*
> *with enjoyment."*
> *BRILLAT SAVARIN*

While caterers generally consider that introducing new dishes or new styles, like *nouvelle cuisine*, is normal activity, many feel that healthy catering is an unjust imposition on the customer. This often arises because healthy food is seen to be not only different, but also not as 'nice to eat'. It is as though healthy food were medicine or, as another ancient wisdom has it, 'if it is doing you good, it can't be enjoyable'. Some people even associate healthy eating only with vegetarianism which a minority still see as a faddist diet eaten only by rabbits and masochists. That leads to the 'healthy eating is for them, not me' school of thought. It just shows how a little misconception goes a long way.

Every caterer, whatever their circumstances, can be a healthy caterer. Remember that the aim is to identify and correct unhealthy changes that have occurred to the national eating pattern. Everyone in the population, each one of your customers, will benefit from healthy foods and not only the few at high risk of illness. Nor do you have to be an idealist; healthy food can benefit you commercially as well as bring professional pride and satisfaction. The path forward for caterers is easy and can be adopted in any kitchen, for any group of customers or clients.

Before getting down to practical matters, it is worth being clear about what is meant by healthy eating. As Chapter 2 showed, the present average diet is unhealthy. The worse a person's diet now, the better off they will be with healthy eating. But even those who feel they now eat healthily will benefit because it will be easier to find good healthy foods.

The aim is to correct the eating pattern, not to create a new way of eating. Traditional foods and dishes which people enjoy are not dismissed, and nothing is forbidden. For caterers it means choosing ingredients with attention to health as well as the conventional criteria of good quality; items like saturated fats, sugar and salt should be reduced. Catering for health can be seen as another element of the skill and judgement which go to make customers appreciate their meals. It should be as much a part of the culinary art as is the blending of taste, texture and colours, the cooking to perfection and the serving of food which appeals to more senses than taste alone. Managers boast of the cleanliness of their kitchens and the hygiene standards in cooking and handling foods. Why should they not be equally insistent that their meals are health-promoting as well as free of health-threatening bacteria?

WHAT IS HEALTHY FOOD?

Understanding the basic principles of healthy eating and being able to use them with the calmest confidence is within the reach of every caterer. There is no need for a university degree or a kitchen library of text books before you can become an expert. The essential qualification is a trust in your own common sense. But for success, many misleading notions of health and eating must be rejected first.

Advice to 'eat a variety of foods' does not help caterers make healthy decisions. Their regular activities include maintaining a stores list which can include hundreds of items. How many is 'variety' – two, twenty-two? Does it mean five courses in a meal, having three or more vegetables, or providing bread and meat and fruit? Perhaps the only examples of diets without variety are those of breast-fed children and hospital patients on a drip feed.

Another vague favourite is 'eat in moderation'. A Department of Health booklet called *Eating for Health* went further with this approach and added that, 'enough is enough; more is not better and can be harmful.' At first sight this sounds sensible and has a comforting aftertaste. But of course, it is absolutely useless advice and cannot be applied. What is moderate? When is 'enough' and how much 'more' is more than enough? A more technical sound comes with advice to 'eat a balanced diet' which is often heard from home economists and even dietitians. But it is no more useful. Although the idea of balance conveys the reassurance of both a scientific formula and precision, no useful definitions can be found in the literature and the notion of balance is also impossible to apply in the kitchen. Before caterers can alter their recipes, they must know what is to be balanced and know when a 'balance' has been achieved, or not. Such guidance is nowhere to be found. Perhaps the term 'balance' should be kept for kitchen scales.

Advice must first be understood, but if it can't be applied when understood, it has no value. The forms of simplistic advice discussed above can be worse than useless; they can have a negative effect. They can lull caterers into the false belief that their present dishes and menus are already healthy. After all, who doesn't eat a variety of foods, consider themselves moderate in all things, and pride themselves on being able to achieve a suitable balance? But worse, such advice cannot be used to help caterers judge how healthy or unhealthy their recipes and menus are.

A brief reflection on the daily work in any kitchen suggests what form useful dietary advice should take. For a start, catering is about numbers. From the quantities of commodities purchased, through the amounts of each ingredient in recipes, to yield, and budgets. What is needed is advice which is both crystal clear and more relevant to caterers' needs. Vague descriptions like 'eat less of' or 'go easy on the salt' are useless. Helpful advice must be scientifically sound and expressed in *quantities* which caterers can use. The basics are simple and NACNE advice is the best reference point for designing clear principles for caterers to follow.

FROM NUTRITION ADVICE TO HEALTHY MENUS

Many people, not only caterers, have difficulty in picturing how to convert advice on nutrition or healthy eating into action in the kitchen. The link is made clear if the business of eating is seen *always* as three separate elements. The elements relate to the daily work of caterers:

1 FOODS are single items which may be bought or prepared in a kitchen. They include farm produce like apples and chicken, manufactured items like bread, margarine and pork pies. Of course foods can be combined as the ingredients of more complex foods or dishes, like coq au vin, a salad or trifle.

2 MEALS are foods that are eaten together on one occasion. Whether it is a continental breakfast, a ten-course banquet, one of the so-called three main meals of the day or one of the more popular snack-type meals taken on the bus to work, a meal usually comprises more than one food. Of all the meals eaten in a year, or lifetime, each has a very slight lasting effect on health – so small it can't be measured. But the effect of each meal added to the next and the one after that becomes very important for health.

3 THE TOTAL DIET includes all the foods and drinks in all meals eaten. When added together, all meals can describe the eating habits or dietary pattern of individuals or whole populations. This is the most important aspect of eating when it comes to health. The diet of hospital patients during a two-week stay will affect their recovery from illness; what mothers eat prior to conception and during the nine months of pregnancy will affect the health of mother and baby; the canteen meals of an office worker over a possible 45 years devoted service will influence the chances of a heart attack before retirement.

The importance for caterers of the three elements is clear. A healthy body needs nutrients but it is foods that are eaten. The foods chosen, how they are combined in dishes and meals, and the range and quality of dishes in different menus have a much more important and longer lasting effect on customers than their enjoyment of your culinary skills. With caterers providing at least 20 per cent of all food eaten, it is no exaggeration to say your customers' health is in your pans. *The caterer can have more influence on people's health than the nutritionist or doctor.*

Chapter 2 discusses the nutrients which are known to be important for health and shows the composition of a healthy diet. But just as a car manufacturer's spare parts list is insufficient to build a car, much less to have it running efficiently, caterers need the list of essential nutrients translated into a caterer's operating manual. The rest of this section provides that manual.

FOUR-WAY CODE OF HEALTHY EATING

Healthy catering is based on four simple actions caterers can control. They can be used one at a time, or in any combination depending on the circumstances and opportunities offered to the caterer. There is no rule for when an action should be taken nor for how much change to make. These decisions are left to the skill and creativity of caterers.

Each of the four actions can be applied to single foods, dishes or menus:

1 *Eating more or less* of particular foods. Foods or dishes which are healthier can be eaten more often or in larger amounts than the less healthy foods.
2 *Substituting* healthier foods or ingredients for less healthy. For example, using soya oil instead of animal fat in frying, using fruit in natural juice

rather than sugar syrups, using low-fat milks, and using more fish and poultry and less fatty cuts of red meat or meat products.

3 *Changing recipes or methods.* Here caterers' skills can shine. It means grilling rather than frying, replacing some of the meat in casseroles with pulses, and using sauces which don't rely on butter or cream, not adding salt to every pan of vegetables before cooking, and increasing the proportion of wholemeal flour in pastry.

4 *Introducing new foods* can add variety and bring healthy options. New vegetables like mange-tout peas or okra, and exotic foods like tofu and Quark are typical and popular examples, but creating or introducing new recipes using common ingredients are also ways of bringing new foods to menus.

These actions, used singly or in any combination, allow the composition of the diet to be modified towards the healthy diet guidelines. Each and every step taken according to the code can improve the dish, meal or diet by correcting any unhealthy features. *The aim is to* move towards a healthier diet *and not expect to arrive in one bold, sudden leap at some form of optimum healthy diet – it doesn't exist.* The code also relies on and encourages the professional skill of caterers. The code can be applied through the daily functions of selecting ingredients, analysing nutritional content of recipes and modifying where necessary and, finally, producing healthy menus.

COMMODITIES AND INGREDIENTS

What comes into the storeroom determines what goes onto the plates. Methods of preparation and cooking as well as the combination of ingredients also determine the nutritional quality of foods but unhealthy commodities are a handicap to the best chefs.

Convenience, cost and availability are major influences on what commodities are bought. Health quality is rarely demanded by caterers and hence is not generally seen as important to suppliers who rarely offer easy options for healthy caterers. Basic choices can have a large effect on the amounts of fat, salt, sugar and fibre entering the storeroom.

MEAT AND MEAT PRODUCTS

Meat is the most expensive item in the total commodity cost. It is also both an important component of most caterers' menus and a major source of avoidable fat, especially saturated fat. Table 5 shows the range of fat contents of different meats and poultry in the raw state. The amount of saturated fat in meats varies slightly, but for catering purposes it is best considering all meat fats as saturated and worth cutting down.

Table 5 Amounts of total fat in raw meats and poultry

Meat		Total fat (g per 100 g meat or % by weight)	Meat		Total fat (g per 100 g meat or % by weight)
Bacon	lean meat	7.4	Duck	lean meat	4.8
	gammon	18.3		meat and skin	42.7
	back rashers	41.2	Turkey	lean meat	2.2
Beef	lean meat	4.6		meat and skin	6.9
	rump steak	13.5			
	brisket	20.5	Offal	brain (lamb)	7.6
	silverside	14.2		heart (lamb)	5.6
	topside	11.2		kidney (pig	2.7
	mince	16.2		and lamb)	
Lamb	lean meat	8.8		liver (calf)	7.3
	loin chops	35.4		oxtail	10.1
	leg	18.7			
	scrag and neck	28.2	Meat	products	
				corned beef	12.1
Pork	lean meat	7.1		ham	5.1
	chops	29.5		luncheon meat	26.9
	leg	22.5		sausages beef	24.1
Veal	fillet	2.7		pork	32.1
Chicken	lean meat	4.3			
	meat and skin	17.7			
	leg (bone in)	3.4			

Source: McCance and Widdowson, *Composition of Foods*, Southgate, D. A. T., and Paul, A. (eds), 4th revised edition, London, HMSO, 1978.

Notice the wide range of fat contents between meats. Lamb and pork cuts tend to be fattier than beef while chicken is leanest of all. With cuts like rump steak most fat is visible and easy to cut off but with scrag or mince, the fat is either in less discrete deposits or too well mixed with the lean to give any chance of trimming the excess before cooking. Lean rump is more expensive than lean brisket, but lean rump is much more cost-effective than fatty rump since there is less wastage and customers tend to be more appreciative. Poultry meat is cheaper and less fatty than red meats which suggests increasing the use of poultry at the expense of red meats and meat products like sausages and mince.

It is possible to specify the fat content of any meats when calling for tenders to supply. Nutritional specification is discussed below.

FISH

Even fatty fish like mackerel and herring are very low-fat compared to fatty meats. Fish oils are also very low in saturated fats and contain useful amounts of the particularly beneficial polyunsaturated fatty acids known as the omega (ω) 3 series. All fish are good alternatives to meat as sources of protein and other nutrients. Smoked, dried and tinned fish tend to be very high in salt – see Table 6.

Table 6 Amounts of total fat and sodium in fish

Fish	Total fat (g per 100 g food or % by weight)	Sodium[1] (mg per 100 g food)
Cod fillet, raw	0.7	77
smoked, raw	0.6	1170
dried, boiled	0.9	400
Haddock, fresh, raw	0.6	120
Lemon sole, raw	1.4	95
Plaice, raw	2.2	120
Herring, raw	18.5	67
Kipper, baked	11.4	990
Mackerel, raw	16.3	130
Pilchards, canned in tomato sauce	5.4	370
Salmon, raw	12.0	98
smoked	4.5	1880
Sardines, canned in oil	13.6	650
Prawns, boiled	1.8	1590
Fish fingers, frozen	7.5	320

[1]Note that 1 g common salt contains 390 mg sodium.
Source: McCance and Widdowson, *Composition of Foods*, Southgate, D. A. T., and Paul, A. (eds), 4th revised edition, London, HMSO, 1978.

DAIRY PRODUCTS

Meat and dairy products are the biggest contributors of both total and saturated fats to the average diet. They supply 50 per cent of the total fat but 62 per cent of the saturated fat (see Appendix IV). The proportion of saturated fats is higher because meat and dairy fats are the most saturated fats in the diet. It makes good sense to cut down these fats. With the exception of butter, other dairy commodities are available in low-fat varieties.

Skimmed and semi-skimmed milks are now readily available and are accepted in drinks and on cereals. Only about 10 per cent of all milk drunk in the UK is taken neat which is when people are most likely to notice any taste differences. But remember, the important issue is not whether the customer can detect any difference in taste, but whether they care! Make sure pasteurised not UHT, long-life or sterilised milks are purchased as these latter have off flavours; the higher the fat content, the more the off flavour. Low-fat milks are interchangeable with full-fat (silver-top, red-top) in all cooking. Skimmed powdered milk is a cheap and convenient way of cooking with milk. Where low-fat milks may lead to a slightly different texture in a product, skimmed milk powder can be added. These powdered milks can be used in concentrations greater than required merely to reconstitute liquid milk which adds more protein and cannot be distinguished from fresh liquid milk in cooking.

Despite the abundance of sauces based on cream, this ingredient is rarely essential for either the taste or structure of sauces. Single cream is 18 per cent fat, whipping is 35 per cent and double cream is 48 per cent fat. The fat is also 66 per cent saturated which is very high so is a good incentive to look for substitutes. Try the low-fat yoghurts, the very low-fat fromage frais, fromage blanc, Smetana and Quark which are all soft cheeses having between 1 and 8 per cent fat, or blended cottage cheese (1–7 per cent fat). Strained Greek yoghurts are up to 10 per cent fat but are excellent cream substitutes because their flavour is more subtle and less acid than British-style yoghurts. Beware of powdered or liquid non-dairy creams which can be rich in saturated vegetable fat. These offer a range of textures and flavours which quickly remind one that the popularity of cream is based on a mixture of its luxury status and plain habit. Good health is a luxury most people are now deciding they cannot do without. Keep cream for special occasions.

Cheeses cover a remarkable range of fat contents and it is not surprising that most people do not know which is which. Cheddar, for example, has nearly twice the fat of brie or camembert. Part of the confusion lies with the continental system of labelling fat with *matière grasse* values and part with the lamentable fact that cheeses do not have to carry any information about their fat content on the label. *Matière grasse* is a measure of the amount of fat in *dry matter*, not the fresh weight of cheese as bought. It is a measure of the amount of milk solids used in making the cheese and serves as a quality mark for consumers. All cheeses made with full-fat milk only and no added cream or skimmed milk will have a *matière grasse* of approximately 45 per cent.

Table 7 Fat in cheeses

Danish	% fat by weight	French	% fat by weight
Blue	29	Tartare	35
Danbo	26	Tomme au Raisin	25
Esrom	24	Vacherin	40
Havarti	24	Vacherol	27
Samsoe	24	Valembert	28
Tybo	26	Vieux Pané	29
Dutch		German	
Edam	22	Bavarian blue	41
Gouda	22	Biarom	24
Leiden	22	Cambozola	42
		Fraisy	25
French		Limburger	15–30
Baby Bel	20	Tilsiter	24
Bleu d'Auvergne	25		
Bon Bel	20	Italian	
Bon Blanc	0	Bel Paese	29
Brie	23	Caccetta	24
Camembert	23	Dolcelatte	28
Chaource	18	Fontina	24
Chaume	27	Gorgonzola	24
Chèvre	23	Mozzarella	24
Coulommiers	20	Parmesan	18
Excelsior	34	Provolone	23
Gervais Petit Suisse	11	Ricotta	20
Marcaire	27	Taleggio	29
Munster	27	Mascarpone	40–45
Neufchatel plain	23		
Port Salut	26	Norwegian	
Pré Clos	28	Jarlsberg	27
Pyrénées	25		
Rigottes des Alpes	25	Swiss	
Roquefort	32	Alpenzell	24
St Albray	28	Emmenthal	24
St André	40	Gruyère	24
Saint Nectaire	25	Raclette	28
Saint Paulin	20	Royalp	24
Suprême	34		

Source: Robbins, C. J., Eating for Health, London, Granada, 1985.

A cream-enriched brie could have a value of 60 per cent but that measures solids. Brie is softer cheese than cheddar and thus has more liquid than a drier cheese like cheddar. It is as though the fat in fresh brie is diluted which is why, pound for pound, brie has less fat (23 per cent) than cheddar (35 per cent) as bought for eating.

Table 7 lists common cheeses available in the UK with their fresh weight contents of total fat. For cooking use cheese sparingly or use smaller amounts of strong-flavoured varieties like parmesan. For the cheese board, include lower-fat types like bries which are not enriched, gorgonzola, Gouda, and the new low-fat types of traditional English hard cheeses like cheddar. Vegetarian cheddar is available but has the same fat as normal cheddar unless the label says otherwise. Use smaller quantities of high-fat cheeses like Stilton and Lymeswold which are about 40 per cent fat.

CEREALS AND FLOURS

Cutting back on fat often means replacing some of the calories lost from the diet. The amount of calories lost can be surprisingly high and cereals are a recommended replacement so more will be appearing in healthy recipes and on menus. By eating less fat, people can eat more cereal foods without increasing their total calorie intake.

Whole cereals, as either flour or the grains, are better for health than the refined products but don't be dragooned into believing that all cereals must always be whole. This is not necessary for health and can cause nightmares for caterers. The message is to use more cereal foods and more of the whole cereals, and there are obvious opportunities.

A range of breakfast cereals is desirable but increase the number of whole-cereal types, especially those without added sugar and salt. Packet cereals like Weetabix, Shredded Wheat, Puffed Wheat, oat porridge and some pre-mixed mueslis have two to three times the dietary fibre of the highly refined breakfast cereals like cornflakes, rice crispies. More processed types like All Bran and Special K may also have fibre, but they also tend to be higher in added salt and sugar. Many packet mueslis are also high in sugar and salt, despite the health image. Check the label and do not be seduced by those available in single-portion packets. Don't be overimpressed by the lists of added vitamins on the packaging. Most ready-to-eat breakfast cereals contain vitamin and mineral supplements which are aimed to replace those lost during processing. Some have amounts above the original whole cereal but they are not 'more healthy' on that account and usually lose out because of the added salt and sugars. Mueslis are more popular and excellent *à la maison* mixes can be concocted with rolled oats, dried fruits and nuts.

Wheat flours are the most common flour used. Wholemeal can be used for breads, shortcrust pastry, scones and many cakes and biscuits. There is no reason why mixtures of whole and white flour should not be used to get best results. Finely ground wholemeal makes better short pastry than the common coarser grades.

Flours like cornflour, chickpea and soya, and arrowroot, are valuable in baking and for thickening. Arrowroot is useful as a glaze to replace sugar.

Bulgar, cracked (or kibbled) wheat and couscous are wheat products which are useful as the basis for salads and also in hot dishes where boiled rice might be used.

Whole grains like wheat, rice, rye, millet and oats are very useful in vegetable dishes, casseroles and stews for thickening and additional textures, and in salads. Brown rice is more nutritious, but there is no reason why polished white rices can't have their place, either for their contribution to colour or their flavours (e.g. basmati rice).

Pastas have come much further than the journey from Napoli to Dover docks. What was once limited to white spaghetti or macaroni now stretches to well over thirty different shapes, sizes, colours and textures. Pastas are useful as dishes on their own, in soups and stews, and in salads. Wholemeal varieties of the more popular shapes are now available.

PULSES

These include peas, beans and lentils and offer a highly nutritious and versatile range of alternatives in dishes where meat is being reduced or replaced. They are cheap and easy to prepare and offer many colours, tastes and textures. Cooking times after soaking vary from 20 minutes to 2 hours and much less in a pressure cooker. Blackeyes, lentils, mung beans and aduki beans do not require soaking and also cook quickly. Do not buy pulses more than one year after harvesting as they quickly get tough and cooking times get longer and less predictable.

FRUIT AND VEGETABLES

The fresher the better for flavour and nutrition. Preparation times and cost deter many caterers from using fresh vegetables but the advantages for healthy eating and customer appreciation are well founded. Tinned vegetables are lower in nutrients and usually have salt or sugar added. Some even contain colouring. Frozen vegetables lose some vitamins during the blanching process before freezing, but they are as good, if not better nutritionally than fresh vegetables which have been sitting around in the supplier's storeroom for a week or two before sitting around in a caterer's own for another week. Prepared vegetables like chipped potatoes, sliced carrots and chopped cabbage are better than tins even though they may come with added preservatives.

The 'good old spud' deserves a revival. It is a very acceptable way of replacing some of the energy removed from the diet by cutting down fat. Make sure though that they are not cooked with loads of fat! Potato starch is also useful as an ingredient in scones, pancakes and in wholemeal pastry to make it shorter.

Many vegetables require little preparation – okra, spinach, sweet corn, cauliflower, mushrooms, courgettes, broccoli, Chinese leaves, leeks, new potatoes – and with the growing interest in vegetarian food offer a wide scope of cheap, healthy and practical dishes like ratatouille, fresh soups and 'stir-frys'. The ease of preparation and simplicity of many vegetable recipes places them firmly in the true convenience food bracket.

Fruit salads using tinned fruit in syrups are a standby for one of the three puddings required on many industrial canteen and too many hotel menus. Switch to fruit in natural juice where suppliers are available but better still consider fresh fruit. With the variety of high quality tropical and other imported fruits supplementing the domestic supply, fresh fruit on the menu is popular and practical.

Buy the freshest of high-quality produce and cut wastage. The art is in combining choice of fruit and vegetables in season and a good relationship with a supplier where high and consistent quality can be negotiated with acceptable prices.

DRIED, PACKET MIXES

Convenience for many caterers means a storeroom crammed with dried mixes for puddings, soups, sauces, cakes and crumbles, gravy and, of course, powdered custard. Many caterers rely on a repertoire of mixes and the water tap to prepare a large proportion of their dishes. Mixes may have a place, but only at three major costs to caterers and their customers:

● First, they are high in salt, sugar and many other additives which usually include both artificial colour and flavourings. Unnecessary additives which prop up the colour, texture or flavour of foods are a handicap to healthy eating. They are usually most prolific on the labels of highly refined foods and are there to replace what has been taken out of the original food during processing and manufacture. The more additives, the less remains of what we all recognise as food. This is another reason for dropping the glib advice to 'eat a balanced diet', meaning plenty of variety. The more additive-rich foods that make up the 'variety', the less of the original nutrient content of the food goes towards the diet. There is a strong movement among consumers away from additives.

● Second, whatever is in the mix as bought ends up in the dish. The caterer has no choice to modify the composition of mixes apart from the volume of water added. This can be a serious constraint in reducing salt or sugar, for example.

● Third, mixes take away the skill of caterers and cooks who are left with little opportunity to be creative.

Use packet mixes only when there is no other reasonable alternative.

SUGAR

Sugar is sugar; it is a common chemical name which includes sucrose from cane or beets and the glucose and fructose powders or syrups which are used mainly in the confectionery industry. All sugars should be treated the same from the health point of view. There is no significant difference for health between the white sugar crystals and any brown sugar. Do not be misled into thinking honey is a healthy food unless you are feeding it to honey bees for which it was designed. All packet sugars, honey and syrups should feature less on storeroom shelves.

Use more fresh and dried fruits, fruit juices or fruit purées to sweeten dishes. Sugar can be halved in most recipes where its only function is sweetening. Artificial sweeteners like Aspartame and saccharine can be used to replace much of the sugar used in prepared foods and beverages. Have individual portions of both artificial sweeteners and sugar available for customers' own selection.

HERBS AND SPICES

Herbs and spices assume a greater importance in healthy cooking because they provide additional flavours to the increasing amount of vegetable, pulse and pasta-type dishes found on healthy menus. Break away from the basic four – bay leaves, thyme, rosemary and sage – especially when bought in standard mixes. There is now a wide variety of dried and fresh herbs available and they are invaluable for fresh and interesting dishes. Fresh herbs can be bought to suit menu plans. A serviceable list of herbs and spices might begin with:

HERBS	SPICES
BASIL	ASAFOETIDA
BAY LEAVES	CARAWAY SEEDS
BERGAMOT	CARDAMOM SEEDS
BORAGE	CAYENNE PEPPER
BOUQUET GARNI	CELERY SEEDS
CHERVIL	CHILLIS
CHIVES	CHINESE FIVE SPICE
CORIANDER LEAVES	CINNAMON
DILL	CLOVES
FENNEL LEAVES	CUMIN
FENUGREEK LEAVES	CURRY POWDERS
FINES HERBS	FENNEL SEEDS
GARLIC	FENUGREEK SEEDS
LEMON BALM	GARAM MASALA
LOVAGE	GINGER ROOT
MARJORAM	JUNIPER BERRIES
MINT	MIXED SPICE
MIXED HERBS	MUSTARD SEEDS
NASTURTIUMS	NUTMEG AND MACE
OREGANO	PAPRIKA
PARSLEY	PEPPERCORNS
ROSEMARY	POPPY SEEDS
SAGE	SAFFRON
TARRAGON	STAR ANISE
THYME	TURMERIC
WINTER SAVORY	VANILLA PODS

Many herbs can be grown easily in the roughest of conditions such as might be available to caterers – small gardens, roof terraces, sunny corners between buildings and in window boxes. Most herbs are very attractive plants, and come in sizes from small chives to tall clumps like lemon balm or lovage. They take up little space, are excellent in filling otherwise wasted space, and thrive without much pampering.

FOOD LABELLING

Caterers and the general public alike suffer from poor food labelling regulations in the UK. It is bad enough that not all commodities bought in are required to have ingredients listed, but the nutritional composition is not required except in exceptional cases like diabetic foods. These shortcomings make it difficult for caterers to be sure that they are buying healthy stores.

Most foods must carry a list of their ingredients in order of weight. All packed foods must also carry on the packaging a statement of the net weight or volume of contents. However there is no way of telling *how much* of an ingredient is in a food by a simple list of ingredients together with the total quantity in the container. As if this wasn't frustrating enough, many foods are exempt from listing their ingredients. The list is available in the *Food Labelling Regulations 1984* available from HMSO. Exempt foods include:

- Fresh fruit and vegetables, including potatoes unless they have been peeled or chipped.

- Cheese, butter, fermented milks and cream to which no other ingredient has been added except enzymes, cultures, etc. With cheese like cheddar, brie, etc., the salt used in manufacture does not have to be listed.

- Food flavourings, whether 'natural' or synthetic.

- Foods consisting of a single ingredient, including flour which can have compulsory additives like calcium, iron, nicotinic acid, and thiamine.

- Alcoholic drinks with an alcohol content less than 1.2 per cent by volume.

Many manufacturers now include some nutritional information on food sold in the retail trade. Very few commodities aimed at caterers carry any nutritional labelling. Such information, however, is not as helpful as it may appear at first sight. Few manufacturers give a full list of nutritional information. Added sugars are usually left off nutrition lists on ready-to-eat cereal packets even though sugar may appear more than once in the ingredients list. Another problem is that there is no agreed manner of presenting this information, so different manufacturers' labels contain different information, expressed in different ways and are thus difficult or impossible to compare.

The MAFF have introduced guidelines for Voluntary Nutritional Labelling. These are intended to guide any manufacturer wishing to add nutritional information to what the law requires to be on labels. The MAFF guidelines allow one of four different lists of nutrients to be used, depending on how much detail a manufacturer chooses to present. The four lists are:

1 Energy (or calories), protein, carbohydrate and fat.
2 Energy, protein, carbohydrate and fat (broken down to show saturates).
3 Energy, protein, carbohydrates (broken down to show total sugars), fat (broken down to show saturates), sodium, and fibre.
4 The same as 3 but with a choice of two optional additions:
   (i) starch as one of the breakdown components of carbohydrates;
   (ii) trans and/or polyunsaturates may also be shown in the breakdown of fat.

The MAFF guidelines *do not include* minerals and vitamins in the nutritional panel, and specifically state that graphic presentation and codes indicating HIGH, MEDIUM and LOW ratings against nutrients are not allowed.

The potential for misleading and confusing labels is readily seen from a stroll down any supermarket food shelves. For example, list 1 could be used on a food rich in sugar, saturated fat and salt while being depleted of fibre and the nutritional list would have no information about any of these nutrients. The same label would have the full backing of the MAFF and the manufacturer could boast that their labels 'comply fully with government standards'. More improvements are necessary before the MAFF guidelines provide useful information for anyone interested in buying for healthy eating. The minimum of useful information on a label should include the nutrients in Example 1, a model digestive biscuit label:

Example 1 Chocolate-coated digestive biscuits

Nutrition information 100 g provides	
Energy	493 calories (2071 KJ) ■
Fat	24.1 g ■
(of which saturates 12.5 g)	■
Carbohydrates	66.5 g ■
(of which sugars 28.5 g)	■
Protein	6.8 g ◨
Sodium	450.0 mg ◨
Fibre	3.5 g ☐
Calcium	84.0 mg
Iron	2.1 mg
Nicotinic acid	1.3 mg
Riboflavin	0.11 mg

■ High; ◨ Medium; ☐ Low

This label includes only those minerals and vitamins which are present in amounts which would supply at least 5 per cent of the Recommended Daily Amounts from the quantity of food someone could reasonably eat in one day. This stops a manufacturer giving a long list of every conceivable nutrient which, although impressive, can be very misleading if many of the nutrients are in insignificantly small amounts. The HIGH, MED, LOW codes are based on calculations which take account of the actual content of the food and how the food contributes to the total diet. There is no standard yet for these codes, but it would not be difficult to develop a workable set of values to apply to food labels. There are already similar codes which regulate the amount of fat or lean meat in sausages or the fat in different liquid milks. The only difficulty lies in getting the industry to agree to provide this useful information.

FOOD COMPOSITION TABLES

Food composition tables offer a convenient way for caterers to assess the nutritional composition of unlabelled commodities. The best available tables are the McCance and Widdowson *Composition of Foods* edited by Southgate and Paul, published by HMSO and now in its fourth revision. The tables are based on food analyses in the Norfolk laboratories of the Food Research Institute and are taken as the respected standard by health professionals and government departments. The food tables are being updated by MAFF in collaboration with the Royal Society of Chemistry and new supplements will be published as they become available. Already available are supplements on *Immigrant Foods*, *Amino Acids and Fatty Acids*, and *Cereals and Cereal Products*. They can be obtained from HMSO.

A wide range of foods are included, sometimes as brand names where popular lines are analysed. The data are based on a number of samples and should be taken as representative values, not precise figures. Apart from the fact that manufacturers may have changed their product formulations since the analyses were made, the composition of foods like beef or apples changes with variety, method of feeding and season. But such is the variation added by the ageing of foods before buying and the inevitable losses of nutrients during handling, preparation and cooking that precise data in the tables would still not give precise nutritional values for foods entering caterers' stores, much less the customer's plate.

Appendix V reproduces the food tables for vegetables from carrots to lentils. All analyses are presented per 100 g of food. This is useful for converting to larger quantities, but is also the same as percentage which makes it easy to compare the nutritional values of almost any food. Most foods are shown in the raw and cooked states and there are also analyses of standard recipes for which the ingredients and method are listed in an appendix.

Each food sample is described, giving the number of samples analysed, whether they were in packets, tins or as the fresh food, and how each was prepared before the analysis was made.

The tables present the main nutrients which are likely to be of interest including energy, protein fats, carbohydrates (as starch and sugars), fibre as well as 10 minerals and 13 vitamins. It is also possible to obtain computer software for analysing foods and recipes. These vary in how much data are in the programme and hence how many individual foods as well as how much information on each food are available. Most are based on the McCance and Widdowson standard tables, but check how much of the original detail is included before buying.

The food tables are also invaluable in analysing recipes, which will be considered in Chapter 4.

FOOD INDUSTRY INFORMATION

Manufacturers normally have precise details of both the full ingredients and the nutritional composition of their products. Even when packaging does disclose some nutritional details, caterers can write to the manufacturer or supplier requesting the full information. Cooking oils are an interesting example of a common store item which comes with no nutritional information and often very little on the mixture of oils used. It is increasingly common for these details to be available to dietitians and doctors when requested, but there is no reason why it should not be given to caterers also.

NUTRITIONAL SPECIFICATIONS

Attempts at shifting towards more healthy commodities can be frustrated by either lack of information about the composition of what is on offer or difficulty in finding a source of supply. Caterers have solutions to both in their buying procedures.

The larger the catering organisation, the more important and complex the role of the purchasing officer or department. Whether for fresh fruit, tea or frying oils, it is common for detailed specifications of the desired commodity to be prepared and presented to potential suppliers, either as part of a tendering or to describe an order. At present it is uncommon for any nutritional considerations to appear on these specifications. A typical specification for British bangers might consist of:

Example 2 Pork and beef sausages

Units per pound	thick × 8
	medium × 12
	thin × 16

Synthetic casings to be used
To be packed in poly bags containing
   three pounds in weight
Poly bags to be packed eight per case
Bacteriological specifications:

viable bacterial	cells a max of 5×10^6 per g meat
coliforms	cells a max of 1000 per g meat
E coli	cells a max of 50 per g meat
Staphylococci	cells a max of 500 per g meat
Streptococci	cells a max of 100 per g meat

In addition would be statements about complying with all relevant food legislation, quality of meat, flavourings and cereal together with details of delivery requirements. There is no reason why nutritional needs cannot be included. With sausages, the amount of salt and total fat could be specified. Similarly with poultry, it is possible to specify the added water content, a maximum level of subcutaneous fat, and even to request that no polyphosphates are added to carcasses as they increase the sodium and absorbed water.

Similar nutritional specifications can be worked out for any commodity and for all relevant nutrients. The larger the catering organisation, the more likely the resources for doing the work. But there are good reasons for smaller organisations to co-operate in developing specifications, especially with a small number of items and when a common supplier is used. There is also enormous scope for collaboration among caterers' professional organisations to begin developing such specifications through organisations like the British Dietetic Association or the National Health Service, which has done detailed work for use in NHS contracts.

It is useful to have a way of recording information on food composition so that different products can be easily compared. The NHS has developed an enquiry procedure involving suppliers giving specific information about products on a standard form. The enquiry can cover both ingredients and nutritional composition. These data are useful in comparing existing commodities and either alternative suppliers or new commodities. Appendix VI presents two standard forms developed in the NHS for making such inquiries. They can be modified to suit individual caterers' needs.

CHAPTER FOUR

RECIPE MODIFICATION

*"The discovery of a new
dish is more beneficial to
humanity than the discovery
of a new star."*
BRILLAT SAVARIN

The conception and preparation of successful dishes is the most satisfying part of most caterers' work. The appearance, appeal and customer satisfaction from the finished product are the measures of success.

Although many caterers consider the success of each dish more important than their combined effect on a whole day's diet, healthy catering relies on careful attention to recipes. Don't forget that dishes make up meals but meals add up to the daily diet of customers. The diet cannot be healthy unless it consists of healthy meals with healthy foods. This does not mean that every food or dish eaten must meet the NACNE guidelines. But since the average diet must make changes in the amounts of saturated fat, sugar and salt, the aim is to reduce *unnecessary* or *avoidable* excesses of these in recipes and foods. There is no single formula for doing this and it relies on the skills of the caterers.

Many factors are considered by caterers in assessing a dish or menu. The notion of a balanced menu already includes careful weighing of colour, taste, texture and temperature. How natural to add nutritional criteria! A healthy recipe then becomes one which satisfies both the gastronomic and health criteria. As the recipes collected in this book show, the results should be as interesting and popular with customers as any other recipes – many caterers say they are more popular.

NUTRITIONAL ASSESSMENT OF RECIPES

There is a vast repertoire of healthy recipes. However there are also many which are recognised as being either fattening or otherwise 'unhealthy' and many others which may be thought to be in the healthy category but which could fail a closer inspection. The only way to know is to analyse recipes for their nutritional content.

It is becoming more common now for recipes to be published alongside a nutritional analysis or with a coding to indicate some aspect of nutritional quality. There are computer software packages which can be used or the old faithful, McCance and Widdowson's food tables. Computers are useful and quick if you know what information is included in the package, but the food tables are much more flexible, as information on new ingredients and variations to allow for new cooking methods, etc. can be added by the caterer. These tables are not difficult to use and have the additional advantage of making caterers more familiar with the composition of foods and ingredients. Whatever the system used, the principles of analysis are the same.

The resulting analyses must be seen as guides only. The nutritional values are based on samples and some of the product formulations may have changed slightly since inclusion. But there are more obvious reasons for variation. Cooking methods, even variation between different caterers using the *same* method, can produce significant differences in nutrients. The boiling of vegetables is a common example. The less water used, the shorter the cooking time and the shorter the time between cooking and serving, the more of the heat-sensitive and water-soluble B-group vitamins remain on serving. What goes on the plate must be eaten before the nutrients can be considered useful to customers. The overall effect of healthy recipes must allow for plate waste, especially in long-stay institutions. Some figures for the NHS suggest plate waste may be as high as 30 per cent. This has as much to do with the appetites of patients as with the appeal of the food offered.

NUTRITIONAL ANALYSIS OF RECIPES

Recipes can be analysed using the following procedure:

1 Make sure the quantities of each ingredient and the number of portions allowed are known.
2 Note the nutrients of interest and prepare a table to enter all data extracted from the food tables with one complete row for each ingredient and a column for each nutrient.
3 Look up each ingredient in the tables. Note that entries may be for raw or cooked food, and that the form of ingredient in the tables may not be exactly the same as in the recipe. Make a choice of the closest item listed in the food tables and ask a dietitian to help if in doubt.

4 Data in the food tables are given per 100 g food. Convert the quantities of each nutrient per 100 g to the amount in the recipe by multiplying or dividing as necessary. E.g., if 450 g of lean rump are used in the recipe, multiply all nutrient values given in the tables as X per 100 g by 4.5 to give the quantities in the recipe.

5 When all the necessary nutrients in each ingredient have been extracted from the tables, add up the columns to give the totals for the recipe.

6 To calculate the nutrient content of a portion, divide this total by the recipe yield. *Note that the nutrients per portion will change with the number of portions planned for a recipe*, and *the number actually taken on serving!*

SAMPLE ANALYSES

Three recipes are analysed below to show their content of some important nutrients. Minerals and vitamins which are also of interest to caterers, especially in long-stay institutions like hospitals and the armed forces, could also be added to the analysis from the same food tables.

SAMPLE 1 *Beef Stroganoff (4 portions)*

Ingredients	Energy (cals)	Carbohydrate g	Protein g	Total/ saturated fat g	Sugars g	Fibre g	Sodium mg
steak 400 g	788	–	75.6	54/24.2	–	–	200
butter 50 g	370	–	0.2	41/25	–	–	435
shallot 25 g	na	na	na	na	na	na	na
white wine 125 ml	83	–	–	–	–	–	–
cream 125 ml	265	4	3	26.5/16	4	–	52.2
juice ¼ lemon	na	na	na	na	na	na	na
parsley	na	na	na	na	na	na	na
TOTAL	1506	4	78.8	121.5/65.2	4	–	687.2
PER PORTION	376.5	1	19.7	30.4/16.3	1	–	171.8

NOTES: A dash (–) means that there is an insignificant amount of the nutrient in food or ingredient and 'na' means the nutrient is not normally present in food or ingredient. To convert the mg of sodium to grams of common salt, divide the total sodium by 390 (1950 mg sodium = 5 g salt).

SAMPLE 2 *Yorkshire pudding (4 portions)*

Ingredients	Energy (cals)	Carbohydrate g	Protein g	Total/ saturated fat g	Sugars g	Fibre g	Sodium mg
flour 100 g	350	80.1	9.8	1.2/.2	–	3.4	2
salt 5 g	–	–	–	–	–	–	1950
1 egg	147	–	12.3	10.9/4	–	–	140
milk 250 ml	156.25	11.75	8.25	9.5/5.8	11.7	–	125
dripping 25 g	225	–	–	25/10.8	–	–	5
TOTAL	878.25	91.85	30.35	46.6/20.8	11.7	3.4	2222
PER PORTION	219.6	23	7.6	11.7/5.2	2.9	1	556

SAMPLE 3 *Crème caramel (6 portions)*

Ingredients	Energy (cals)	Carbohydrate g	Protein g	Total/ saturated fat g	Sugars g	Fibre g	Sodium mg
sugar 100 g	375	100	–	–	100	–	–
4 egg yolks	452	–	21	39.7/11.1	–	–	65
water 100 ml	na	na	na	na	na	na	na
milk 500 ml	312.5	23.5	16.5	19/11.6	23.4	–	125
sugar 50 g	188	50	–	–	50	–	–
TOTAL	1327.5	173.5	37.5	58.7/22.7	173.4	–	190
PER PORTION	221	28.9	6.3	9.8/3.8	28.9	–	31.7

FAT, PROTEIN AND CARBOHYDRATE AS PERCENTAGE OF ENERGY

Before commenting on these analyses, it is helpful to introduce one useful way of expressing fat, protein and carbohydrates which can be used to compare foods and diets. The NACNE and COMA recommendations for a desirable diet did not give fat values as weight but as a percentage of the total calories (energy) in the diet. Because everyone has different requirements of energy each day, it makes sense to say what *proportion* of the total energy eaten should come from fat, proteins, carbohydrates, etc. (It is useful to recall that, in Chapter 2, NACNE said not more than 30 per cent of the total energy should come from fat and not more than 10 per cent from saturated fats. This leaves 10–15 per cent of the energy needs to come from protein and a desirable 50–60 per cent to come from carbohydrates, preferably starches and not sugars. About 5 per cent could come, on average, from alcoholic drinks. The total of energy should be only enough for each person's needs which is easily monitored by measuring body weight.) This is more sensible than advising on what weight should be eaten since everyone would be eating different weights of food and of fat, protein, etc. in achieving their total energy for a day. Advice on the desirable proportions stays constant over the normal range of amounts of food eaten by healthy people. This means the same *composition* of diet applies to all healthy people. Of course people at special risk of disease or who are on diets advised by doctors or dietitians need special food, but they are a small proportion of most caterers' customers and should also receive their own healthy diets.

The energy (or calories) in foods and ingredients are given in the food tables in two different units: kcal is short for kilocalories which are known commonly as calories; the other is kJ which is kilo Joules, the metric measure of energy. 1 kcal = 4.184 kJ. Sometimes energy is expressed as MJ or mega Joules; 1 MJ =, 1000 kJ.

To convert from kcal to kJ, multiply by 4.184.
To convert from kJ to kcal, multiply by 0.24.

Fat, protein, carbohydrate and alcohol can be converted to energy values as follows:

1 g fat provides 9 kcal (or 37 kJ)
1 g protein provides 4 kcal (or 17 kJ)
1 g carbohydrate provides 3.75 kcal (or 16 kJ)
1 g alcohol provides 7 kcal (or 29 kJ)

Converting the fat, protein and carbohydrate in the beef Stroganoff recipe to energy values is as follows:

per portion	g	calculation	energy kcal
carbohydrate	1	1 × 3.75	= 3.75
protein	19.7	19.7 × 4	= 78.8
fat	30.4	30.4 × 9	= 273.6
TOTAL			356 kcal

Looking back to the recipe analysis table, the total energy in the beef Stroganoff recipe is 376 kcal per portion not 356 kcal. The difference is due to the 125 ml of white wine in the recipe which contributed 83 kcal to the total energy of the recipe, or 20 kcal per portion.

The percentage contributions to energy are calculated using the energy conversions just above as follows:

$$\text{carbohydrate as \% total energy is } \frac{3.75 \times 100}{376} = \quad 0.1\%$$

$$\text{protein as \% total energy is } \frac{78.8 \times 100}{376} = \quad 21\%$$

$$\text{fat as \% total energy is } \frac{273.6 \times 100}{376} = \quad 73\%$$

$$\text{Total } 94.1\%$$

(Note that the total would be 100% if the alcohol was included. It gives 5.3 per cent of the total energy.)

Any reader who doubts that the *proportions* of fat, protein and energy remain the same whatever the *amount* to the beef Stroganoff recipe is prepared, should calculate the percentages using the total yield figures from Sample 1 using the calculation above. The figures should be the same as those calculated for each portion above. This is a useful exercise which will show your grasp of the calculations.

The same calculations for the other two recipes gives the following summary analysis expressed in proportions of energy from fat, protein and carbohydrate.

Comparison of fat, protein and carbohydrate in the sample recipes

Recipe	total energy per portion kcal	% energy from fat	% energy from protein	% energy from carbohydrate
Beef Stroganoff	376	73	21	0.1
Yorkshire pudding	219	48	14	39
Crème caramel	221	40	11	49

WHAT DO THE ANALYSES TELL THE CATERER?

BEEF STROGANOFF RECIPE

This recipe has over one ounce (30.4 g) of fat per serving which is high and over half this fat is saturated. Although the energy supplied per portion is not high for such a dish, 73 per cent of that energy is from fat. This is unnecessarily high and a glance back at the recipe shows where the excess fat comes from. The butter and cream make up over half the total fat and both are particularly saturated fats. The butter can be replaced by a much smaller quantity of a polyunsaturated oil, or even dispensed with as it is not necessary to seal the meat before adding the liquid. (Many colleges still teach that meat should be sealed *always* to keep in the juices, but many chefs have made their own comparisons of sealed and unsealed and found no difference.) The cream is a 'touch of luxury' which can be replaced with fromage frais. The effect of 'richness' is the same but the fat contribution is decreased by three quarters. The fat value for steak includes the visible fat as well as that in the lean. Fat on meat varies and it is possible to make significant reductions by trimming.

The recipe is not low in sodium, but the removal of the butter would make a good reduction. The fibre is zero because meat has none and the amounts from the shallot and parsley are insignificant. This dish would normally be eaten with vegetable accompaniments, like potato, which can supply some of the energy removed as fat and would boost the fibre content of the meal.

NOTE: The alcohol supplies 5.5 per cent of the energy in this recipe. This is not a major problem especially since most would be vaporised during cooking, but NACNE recommends it should not be above 4 per cent of the total dietary energy. This meal could well follow alcoholic aperitifs and be eaten with wine, so the total alcohol of the meal is likely to go up.

Beware of using wine, or other alcohols to make up for any energy loss from cutting down fats in the diet. It is healthier, especially when considering foods, to make up any losses with starchy carbohydrate food or even protein foods like pulses or fish. Leave the alcohol to the drinkers, not the eaters.

YORKSHIRE PUDDING

This is an example of a traditional recipe where the unhealthy ingredients are such an integral part that modification may not be acceptable. The batter is baked in dripping which is absorbed into the pudding. The result is that half the energy comes from saturated fat. The salt added is quite high, even for this dish, but it is not uncommon to add so much. None is necessary for a successful product. Leave the addition of salt for the customer. The problem is that Yorkshire pudding is always served with roast meats which also tend to be fatty. This fat could be replaced, but would Yorkshire pudding be the same without the quantity of fat?

Using half low-saturated oil like soya or corn with half the stated amount of dripping will at least cut the saturated fat. Smaller portions will cut the amount of fat in a portion. The pudding can be usefully extended by adding button mushrooms and the rest of the meal could be examined carefully for ways of cutting the fat in the total meal – have jacket potatoes instead of roast and take care to skim off as much fat as possible before making the gravy.

CRÈME CARAMEL

Typical of too many puddings, this recipe contains little else but fat and sugar. Fifty per cent of the energy comes from sugar which is also the only carbohydrate on offer. One third of the sugar is used simply to make the caramel but the 100 g in the custard could be reduced without affecting the texture of the product. The fat from milk could be reduced by using liquid or powdered skimmed milk but the high input of fat (and cholesterol) from the egg yolks is necessary with real custard which is the essence of this dish. There is some scope for reducing both sugar and fat, but one either accepts that crème caramel is a sweet, fatty pudding to have occasionally or replaces it with something healthier.

The yield in the recipe gives good-sized portions which could be reduced with useful benefits to both customer and the accounts. A yield of 8 reduces the amount of sugar and fat eaten by 31 per cent but *not their contributions to the total energy of the dish*. Creativity is a measure of success nowadays and this very traditional dish can be made more acceptable to the health-conscious by serving smaller portions with baked bananas or by extending it with the addition of banana, or other fruit, purée to the caramel or, dare it be said, instead of the caramel?

MAKING THE CHANGES

Any recipe or single food can be analysed as above and both the amount of change and the ingredients where change is necessary are clearly evident. The caterer's skill in altering the recipes while preserving the essential character of the original, or even to produce a novel variation, can then be directed by knowing exactly how much to change what.

There is nothing sacrosanct about recipes. Few chefs follow any recipe precisely as written. Modifications may be introduced because stated ingredients are not available or perhaps are too expensive. Other changes may come about because few chefs measure all ingredients exactly and there is usually a wide leeway for altering quantities before the product is noticeably different. These modifications can produce subtle changes which are both appreciated by customers and identified with the particular chefs.

Modifying recipes for health is also part of the skill of the caterer. Depending on the recipe and how much change is indicated by the nutrient analysis, caterers know what changes to suggest and can test their modifications to see if the resulting product is successful. Many of the recipes in this book are modified versions of existing recipes.

There are two main aims in modifying recipes for health:

- avoiding excess fat, sugar and salt and replacing removed fibre;

- helping customers to make healthier choices by offering healthier dishes.

The wide range of options available for changing the composition of dishes can be classified into the same four types of change which were introduced in Chapter 1.

1 Cutting down on unhealthy ingredients
2 Substituting healthier ingredients
3 Changing composition of ingredients or foods
4 Introducing new ingredients, dishes or foods

Often the four will be combined and some changes may fit into more than one category because several advantages may follow from a single step. For example, replacing some fatty mince with pulses in a cottage pie recipe will reduce fat and increase fibre. This change could be seen as a substitution (pulses for fatty meat) or a change in composition (higher fibre dish) or a new food (the pulse/mince).

REDUCING THE QUANTITY OF INGREDIENTS

There are many simple ways of making significant reductions in the less healthy recipes or cooking methods. The size of the benefits depends on the original recipe and the degree of reduction which is possible without affecting the success of the recipe.

- *Salt should never be added to vegetables during cooking* and should be reduced or eliminated as an ingredient of recipes. The idea that salt is added to every cooked savoury dish is now an unhealthy and unnecessary habit. About 75 per cent of all salt eaten is added to foods in manufacture or cooking before food hits the plate. Leave the customer the choice to add salt.

● *Cut down the amounts of sugar added* to cooked dishes and resist the temptation to heap it into crumble toppings of baked fruit dishes. Sugar is often added in excess of the ability of taste buds to detect any difference and sizable reductions can be made before they can be tasted. Like salt, slow reductions in the amounts of sugar in foods are not noticed and after three weeks or so the original levels in foods are considered too sweet. Food manufacturers often use sugar as a cheap bulking agent; caterers should never follow suit.

● *Do not use butter glazes* for vegetables or add oil to boiled rice. It is much better to batch-cook these dishes frequently to avoid them drying out or sticking before serving.

● *Cut down the use of cream in soups, etc.* Use yoghurts or fromage frais for the same 'richness'.

● *Cut down fat in cooking* by changing cooking methods. Avoid deep-frying foods. Poach, steam, grill or shallow fry (with the merest wipe of a polyunsaturated oil) instead. Don't add butter to all manner of sauces or dishes as though taste depended on this magic ingredient. Don't soften vegetables or brown meat in fat before making soups, casseroles or stews; it has no detectable advantage. Any added colour or 'caramelising' flavours can be added with good quality low-salt stock cubes.

● *Reduce meat fat by avoiding fatty meats (mince, sausages, scrag), trimming visible fat, skinning chickens* before casseroling, skim cooked-out fat from meat dishes and gravies with a spoon or by laying a paper towel on the surface of the hot dish to absorb the surface. Larger-scale cooking can use pipettes to suck up the fat. Smaller quantities of meat can be used in many recipes to reduce fat and ingredient cost.

● *Don't roast vegetables in a sea of fat.* Use a brushing of polyunsaturated oil and bake them in an oiled baking tray.

● *Reduce the amount of cheese in sauces and dishes* by using smaller amounts of higher flavoured cheese or adding the cheese to the top of the dish instead of in the dish. It is surprising how the customer will think they are getting *more* cheese and the dish will taste more cheesy with the cheese in a separate layer rather than dispersed through the dish. A little yellow mustard powder adds colour and brings out the taste of cheddar helping a little cheese go a long way.

● *Cut down on run-of-the-mill stock cubes, and soup, gravy, sauce and pudding mixes.* They are high in sodium from salt, MSG or other technological aids. High quality vegetable stocks which are low in salt and other props are available.

MAKING SUBSTITUTIONS

There are many opportunities for making recipes healthier by simple substitution of one ingredient for another which makes for an equally successful end product. Some substitutions result in slightly different products, but, so long as the customer is happy and the product is made healthier, it must be classified a successful substitution. The list is endless. Some examples are:

SUBSTITUTE	FOR	ADVANTAGES
CONTINENTAL BREAKFAST	*ENGLISH FRIED BREAKFAST*	*less fat, salt and calories*
WHOLEMEAL CEREALS	*REFINED AND SWEETENED*	*increase fibre as well as vitamins and minerals; reduce sugar and salt*
WHOLEMEAL FLOUR	*WHITE*	*increases dietary fibre*
LOW-FAT MILKS, SMP	*FULL-FAT MILKS*	*less fat and calories*
LOW-FAT CHEESES	*FULL-FAT CHEESES*	*less saturated fat and calories*
YOGHURTS, FROMAGE FRAIS	*CREAM*	*75% reduction in saturated fat, total fat and calories*
POLYUNSATURATED OILS	*HARD COOKING FAT*	*major reductions in saturated fat and also of cholesterol; increase in polyunsaturates*
CORNFLOUR, ARROWROOT, PULSE-THICKENED STOCKS AND SAUCES	*FAT-BASED PAN SAUCES AND WHITE, BECHAMEL AND MORNAY-TYPE SAUCES*	*reduction in fat and calories*
PULSE DISHES	*FATTY MEAT DISHES*	*less fat more fibre*
HERBS AND SPICES	*SALT*	*less salt more varied flavours*

SUBSTITUTE	FOR	ADVANTAGES
MADE SOUPS	*PACKET SOUPS*	*less salt*
FISH AND PULSE DISHES	*MEAT DISHES*	*less fat, less saturated fat and more fibre*
VEGETABLES, SALADS	*SOME MEAT DISHES*	*more variety, less fat, more vitamins and fibre*
FRESH FRUITS	*SWEET PUDDINGS*	*more fibre, vitamins and minerals with less sugar, calories and fat*
MUESLI SNACKS	*CHOCOLATE-COATED AND CREAM-FILLED BISCUITS*	*cut fat, increase fibre, vitamins and minerals*
LOW SUGAR JAMS, FRESH AND DRIED FRUIT PURÉES	*JAM, HONEY*	*less sugar, calories*
FRESH FRUIT JUICE, MINERAL WATER, LOW-CALORIE DRINKS	*SOFT DRINKS, ALCOHOL*	*less sugar, alcohol, calories*

CHANGING COMPOSITION OF INGREDIENTS AND DISHES

Most of the changes in the two headings above will alter the composition of dishes but it is often helpful to tackle healthier eating by starting with recipes or dishes and looking for ways of changing their composition.

For example, a popular dish like cottage pie can be improved by:

- using less mince,

- skimming the fat from the cooked mince,

- substituting some haricot, kidney beans or TVP for some of the mince,

- adding more carrot, mushroom, tomatoes or mashed baked aubergines,

- flavouring with herbs and tomato purée, not salt,

- adding cornflour, potato starch or wholemeal breadcrumbs to thicken the mince filling,

- adding very little fat to the creamed potato topping.

Analysing the recipes will show what could be changed with benefit and a simple review of the recipe will present the options. The resulting cottage pie could have half the fat, more fibre and starchy carbohydrate making up some of the lost fat, the same protein content from the pulses, added vitamins from the additional carrots or other vegetables.

In particular, it is very common for recipes to be improved in their composition by looking at:

● The amount and type of fat used as ingredients and in cooking. Fat is an important ingredient in many dishes. While they may be served less often because of their high fat, they can be made more acceptable by reducing the amount of saturated fat in whatever fat is in the food. Changing the type of meat can also change the composition of the fat. Although a Boeuf Bouilli à la Française must include beef, there is no reason why a similar dish with other meats cannot be made under an appropriate name. Consider the advantages of choosing lower fat content or lower saturated fat containing meats (Table 8). Notice how the saturated fat content of red meats does not change much even when the amount of total fat may be reduced. Poultry and fish are notable for having both less total fat and significantly less saturated fats. Using more poultry or fish in dishes will change the fat composition of 'meat dishes'.

Table 8 Fat content and percentage of saturated fatty acids in fat in common meats and fish

meat	fat content of food (% by weight)	saturated fat (% by weight of fat)
beef and veal	15.2	41.2
mutton and lamb	22.0	47.4
pork	23.1	38.2
bacon and ham	29.5	40.4
poultry	4.9	30.0
sausages	28.4	40.0
other meat and meat products	14.1	41.3
fish		
cod fillet	0.7	26.1
mackerel fillet	16.3	27.0

Source: McCance and Widdowson, *Composition of Foods*, Southgate, D. A. T., and Paul, A., 4th revised edition, London, HMSO, 1978.

● Increasing the proportion of wholemeal flour in all flour products from bread to pastry is a good way of shifting upwards the total amount and quality of dietary fibre in meals. Don't be bullied into feeling that 'if it isn't wholemeal, it can't be good enough for you'. The aim is to increase the amount of wholemeal used. Many customers may not like wholemeal bread but enjoy breads which have a mixture of white and wholemeal flours to improve texture. Pastry made with all wholemeal *is* a different product from white-flour pastry. Some uses are more acceptable than others – crisp wholemeal pastry works well with quiches but is not so well accepted in apple pie where shorter pastry is preferred by many. Choose the product and vary the mixtures of flour. So much flour is used in cooking, that changing the composition towards wholemeal where possible is desirable. As well as boosting fibre, the more wholemeal, the more B vitamins and minerals go into the diet.

● Dairy products are a major contributor of fat and saturated fat to all diets apart from vegan diets. They are also one of the easiest food groups to alter the composition of. Apart from butter or ghee which are made from pure dairy fat, all other dairy products are available in low-fat forms, many of which have virtually no fat at all. These low-fat products can be used in all cooking instead of their full-fat parents without any significant effect on the quality of the product. Appendix IV shows that liquid milk alone supplies nearly 10 per cent of the average person's daily intake of fat but 15 per cent of the saturated fat. Remember the NACNE guidelines say that saturated fat should be cut by 50 per cent: just by using only skimmed milks instead of full-fat, one third of the necessary cut in saturated fat is achieved.

Some people make the careless statement that low-fat milks and other products are not liked. The fastest growing dairy product market is low-fat milks, and low-fat cheeses like brie and cottage have been popular for years. Use a little bottle and begin lowering the unnecessary fat in your cooking by changing the composition of dairy products.

● Increase the amount of starchy carbohydrates in dishes by using more root vegetables, cereals like rice or barley, and pulses. These can replace some of the meat, be the base of dishes in their own right, or appear as thickeners in soups, casseroles, stews and sauces. Some of the fat being removed will need replacing with starch to ensure the energy content of meals is sufficient. These carbohydrates are the ones nutritionists advise eating more of and they have a natural place in cooking because of their flavours, textures and other properties. Bread is another good source of carbohydrate and encouraging the once common British habit of having bread on the table for every meal is another easy way of increasing the carbohydrate composition of meals.

● Preparation and cooking methods have a significant effect on composition. Trimming of visible fat from meats and removing the skin of poultry can cut fat by up to 20 per cent before assembly and cooking begins. Potatoes, carrots, and parsnips should be unpeeled where possible and fruits like tomatoes, apples, pears and grapes also are best left unpeeled before cooking or when presented in salads. This will increase both fibre and the general nutritional content of these foods.

All forms of frying introduce additional fat to dishes. Deep frying, even when done properly, leads to a coating of fat and often significant absorption of fat. Deep frying fat also becomes saturated quickly because of oxidation at the high temperatures involved. Repeated heating of the fats makes matters worse as harmful byproducts linked to cancers are produced. Shallow frying is better, but the smallest wipe of fat in non-stick pans is necessary to justify its regular inclusion in healthy catering. Even with the best of intentions, shallow frying too easily becomes a source of avoidable fat. Stir frying, especially of vegetables, is a possible option because it combines very small amounts of fat with rapid cooking, which preserves heat-sensitive nutrients, and does not have the vegetables awash with cooking water which is discarded along with the nutrients leached from vegetables.

The increased use of vegetables in healthy eating makes it the more important to consider their composition during cooking. Half the value of vegetables is in their range of texture, colour and flavours; the other half is their richness in minerals, vitamins, starch and fibre. Boiling of vegetables is the source of one of the most common criticisms of catering foods and is, for the same reason, a cause of much lost nutritional value. Overcooked vegetables lose taste and texture as well as nutrients. Boil vegetables in the minimum of water, add them to boiling water, cook only until they are cooked – which is but a few minutes for greens and not many more for roots and tubers – do not add salt to the water, and cook in batches which allow them to be served as quickly as possible. Use the cooking water in stocks and soups so leached minerals and vitamins don't go down the drain.

Steamers are a good way of cooking vegetables and pressure cookers take away much of the temptation to overwater and overcook while also saving on cooking time and heating bills. Microwaves can be used with smaller batches and are especially useful for green vegetables.

● Sugar seems to be ubiquitous in catering foods. If not in the purchased commodities, it is added as an ingredient. Starchy carbohydrates should be increased at the expense of sugars.

Healthy catering means using more cereals, pulses and root vegetables which increase the starchy carbohydrates and make it possible to cut down on sugars without decreasing the total energy because equal weights of sugars and starch have the same energy content.

The amount of sugars can be reduced by adding less to recipes and choosing low-sugar varieties of ingredients like tinned fruits, jams and preserves, beverages. Many manufactured and processed commodities contain significant amounts of added sugar, the amounts of which are rarely declared on the container. Since over 60 per cent of the population say they try to lose weight each year, there is little fear of customers criticising caterers for reducing the empty calories added to their dishes as sugar. There is no suggestion that sweets and puddings leave the menu, but together with reducing sugar in recipes, fresh fruits, yoghurts etc. could be made a regular alternative.

● Salt can be greatly reduced by the simple expedient of not adding it during cooking. Begin by the rare step of measuring the salt that goes into a dish and slowly reduce the amount going into all cooking over several weeks. The slow reduction will not be noticed and it is possible to reduce the amount of added salt by up to 50 per cent with no effort and without customers detecting the difference. Cutting out stock cubes and packet mixes except for emergencies, reducing the use of salted butter, restricting the use of dried and salted foods like fish, salamis, etc. will help keep the total salt in ingredients low. Lower salt in cooking can be compensated for by using more fresh ingredients and expanding the use of herbs and spices.

EVALUATION OF MODIFIED RECIPES

Any changes to the quality of commodities being purchased or to the recipes need to be tested, first to ensure that the recipe works and is acceptable to customers and, second, to see if the planned improvements in composition have been achieved.

Recipes can be assessed using the food tables as shown earlier in this chapter but a simpler form of test is also available to see how overall composition of food changes. A careful audit of commodities entering the store provides an accurate measure of the amounts of items like sugar, salt, cooking oils, butter and margarine, stock cubes, packet soups, sachets of sugar and artificial sweetener being used. Targets can be set and monitored. For example, to reduce salt by 20 per cent over three months, sugar by

50 per cent over six months and a 30 per cent reduction in the use of cooking oils over six months.

This audit gives a good measure of the cumulative changes across all food served. It is not as accurate as taking samples of foods as cooked and having them analysed in a laboratory but it is a compromise and will give sufficient information for any caterer to check progress in modifying recipes for health.

ARE HEALTHY RECIPES EXPENSIVE RECIPES?

The answer is a little like the curate's egg and even more like 'how long is a string of sausages?' It depends on what dishes are being offered.

However the biggest cost in catering is labour and it is only realistic to accept that, for many, packet mixes and other convenience items are saving either labour time or substituting for a shortage of skilled labour. Many erstwhile healthy caterers are put off by the prospect of increased labour costs in preparation.

Careful planning of preparation and other working areas, judicious use of mechanised equipment for peeling, slicing and chopping vegetables, the use of pressure cookers for pulses and vegetables, and suitable staff training can keep the expected increase in labour costs within budget. The increases are offset against savings in a reduction of total meat used, less cooking-fat consumption as deep fryers get retired to the storeroom (better still, the saleroom), and the greater savings in both wastage and preparation time achieved by using better quality fresh commodities.

There is no reason to believe that healthy catering must be more expensive. There are many caterers in institutional, industrial and commercial catering who have achieved lower costs and higher margins while satisfying their customers. Like all good catering, it requires thought and planning but the results are satisfying and rewarding.

CHAPTER FIVE

PLANNING HEALTHY MENUS

"He who receives guests,
and pays no personal care to
the repast offered them, is
not worthy to have
friends."
BRILLAT SAVARIN

The menu is the first important contact between caterer and customer. Great care should go into both the compilation and presentation of menus. They list the dishes offered and give the necessary information for customers to make their choices – names and descriptions of dishes, prices and some guide to the composition of dishes.

Different types of caterers require different menus – a large hospital menu has little similarity with a high-street restaurant menu. Also different meal occasions require their own specific menu composition – that a banquet menu and a school dinner menu are constructed differently would not be mistaken whatever the quality of the card they were printed on. However, whether written on parchment or chalked on the wall, all these different menus should have common aims when it comes to the customer's health:

● To offer dishes which minimise unnecessary amounts of fat, sugar and salt, and offer a range of important minerals, vitamins and fibre.

● To offer a range of dishes in each course so that customers can make their own choices for health. There is no 'perfect healthy food'. Some popular dishes are less 'healthy' than others, but customers should always have a choice of healthy dishes whatever else is offered.

● To provide sufficient information about the dishes and their composition to ensure that all customers are able to make informed and accurate healthy choices from the menu.

Planning a healthy menu requires the same attention to detail as is given to the balance of colour, texture, flavours, sauces, temperatures, or repetition of ingredients. There need be no conflict between healthy food and enjoyment. The important considerations in planning healthy menus are:

WHAT TYPE OF MENU?

1 *Restaurants, pubs, clubs, hotel dining rooms, banquet halls* are visited irregularly by individual customers. Such establishments are treated like 'grazing' – a meal here, another there. The impact of any single menu on the health of customers is slight but healthy menus can help support their general efforts to eat healthily. Because restaurants are seen often as a treat or an occasion for special meals, this does not mean rich, unhealthy food is either expected or necessary. Lighter food may attract customers other than healthy eaters as they may be among the many weight conscious or who find lighter foods suit their digestion better.

À la carte menus can offer large numbers of dishes and it is not necessary to ensure that *any* combination of dishes is healthy so long as customers can make healthy choices from a clearly marked menu. *Table d'hôte* menus restrict choice to one or two options, but give the caterer a good opportunity to offer a complete healthy meal. The vitamin and mineral content is less important here than total energy and composition in terms of the NACNE guidelines. However, carefully cooked food will both retain more minerals and vitamins and be more appealing to customers because it will taste and look better for the attention.

2 *Workplace canteens and restaurants, and schools* have more influence on customers' total food intake and greater care with the composition of meals is necessary. A third or more of the average person's daily nutrition comes from the mid-day meal. Two or more main meals at work are common with some shift work.

Until 1980, local authorities were required by law to ensure that the school meal had one third of the RDA of all listed nutrients for school-age children. Since this law was changed there has been a fall in the nutritional standards of school meals. A major study on the Diets of Schoolchildren by the Department of Health (DHSS, 1986) concluded that school meals should be improved to help protect children from a general decline in their dietary standards. Another opportunity for caterers to assert their role in the nation's health! Many local authorities have taken steps to improve their school meals and are satisfying their fickle customers, which is an impressive mark of success.

Because they provide a substantial proportion of meals eaten by workers and schoolchildren, caterers should realise both the importance of offering healthy food and the influence they can have on future eating patterns and health. Menus can be planned so that any reasonable combination of dishes provides a healthy meal within the NACNE guidelines. Healthy customers is one thing, but think of the advantages of their living longer and returning to eat again and again and again.

Healthy menus also provide excellent opportunities for promoting healthy eating to customers. The links between caterer and customer are regular and relations are usually good which makes it easier to judge what the customer wants and to explore new healthy dishes and menu combinations. Many schools, hospital staff restaurants and workplace restaurants have begun to provide both healthy menus and information about healthy eating in the dining rooms.

3 *Hospital, prison and armed forces* menus require special consideration. Here the total food intake over weeks, months or years is supplied by the caterer. Any deficiencies can have serious effects on health. Menus should be planned to provide the RDA for minerals and vitamins each day and be within the NACNE guidelines. It is as important to ensure adequate amounts of vitamins as to make sure that the amounts of saturated fat are kept low over time.

Customers in institutions like geriatric or paediatric hospitals are often less able to make their own choices or the catering budgets can constrain the number of choices and the range of commodities the caterer has to plan menus. Caterers in the NHS may have less than £2 per patient per day for food in long-stay hospitals. The caterers are often left with the responsibility for ensuring that their customers are adequately fed, despite the limitation of resources.

Institutional caterers also face special problems which are difficult to accommodate in menu planning. Hospitals are the most obvious as there is both a range of special dietary needs of patients to be met and the food has to be distributed to perhaps 1,000 patients' beds and not only to dining rooms. Plate wastage is high, often because patients have other matters on their mind than appetite – food not eaten cannot nourish. There are difficulties in keeping food hot for the minimum of time before serving which means greater losses of heat-sensitive vitamins as well as flavour. The NHS also has, along with other institutions like schools, the additional burden of EEC subsidies on foods like butter and beef which make it economically difficult to buy healthier alternatives. New technologies like cook-chill have the potential to solve some of these nutritional losses but must be used strictly according to instructions or other difficulties, like increased risk of food poisoning, can be introduced.

Institutional menus run on two- or three-week cycles which should be both nutritionally sound throughout and sufficiently varied to maintain the appetite interest of captive customers.

WHAT IS HEALTHY?

There is no formula giving the precise amounts of each nutrient which should be given in a day's meals, much less in any single dish. Even the RDAs discussed in Chapter 2 give a measure of only the *minimum mineral and vitamin needs for health*. It needs to be remembered too that there may be other vitamins or minerals which are not yet included in the RDA list, but which are still needed for good health. The minerals selenium and chromium are examples. However, in the absence of RDAs for these nutrients, caterers are best using the RDA as their guide in assessing and planning healthy recipes and menus.

Within wide limits, more than the RDA of a nutrient can be eaten with neither harm nor significant benefit and less than the RDA for some vitamins and minerals can be eaten for short periods without harm. Similarly, with the NACNE guidelines for fat, sugar and salt, there was no suggestion that every dish, every meal or every day's diet *must be less than the upper limits* for these items in the diet. Both the RDA and the NACNE figures should be used as a guide and *never* as formulae to be followed precisely.

Institutional menus are a special case and should be planned to have *always* at least the RDA and fit within NACNE. The definition of healthy when applied to other menus is more relaxed. The aim is to make sure menus lean towards, and not away from, the RDA and NACNE guidelines. This will have the effect of the menus moving closer and closer to the guidelines as they are tried and refined with time. The closer to the guidelines the better, but being spot-on is not necessary. This means a menu doesn't fail because it is 37 per cent total energy from fat when NACNE suggests a target of 30 per cent, unless of course the amount of fat has been creeping up with successive menus. Some menus may work out at less than 30 per cent, others slightly above. The important thing is that they stay around 30 per cent and neither stay around 40 per cent nor begin increasing beyond say 35 or 40 per cent!

Steps to achieving healthy menus include:

● Analyse current menus and recipes so you have a good idea of how they compare with NACNE and the RDA. This is a good time to involve your local Health Authority or company dietitian. This analysis will provide an important base-line showing the amount and direction of change for each nutrient or other constituent. The base-line will be useful later on when you assess how much improvement has been made.

● Set targets for each planned change, stating how much change and over what time.

● Get familiar with the foods which contain significant amounts of the important vitamins, minerals and proteins (Appendix I). This will help ensure that the variety of ingredients and dishes presented covers the important nutrients. Match this with seasonal availability of fruits, vegetables and fish to provide foods when they are at their best and cheapest.

● Use the food tables to draw up lists of frequently used foods and other ingredients like cooking oils, etc. to indicate their fat, saturated fat, sugar, fibre and salt contents. With the help of a dietitian these can be classified into HIGH, MED and LOW groups. This list will help identify items to reduce or replace with an acceptable alternative. Keep it on the wall near the menu planner's desk. As recipes are analysed, keep a record of their ingredients and nutritional analyses. This will make compiling healthy menus much easier and quicker.

● Assess progress. Make periodic checks of menus and especially cooking methods to see that they are following the planned changes towards healthier menus and compare progress against targets.

There is nothing quite like real healthy menus to show the principles in action. Evian and the *Caterer and Hotelkeeper* magazine began a monthly national healthy menu competition in 1986 to focus attention on the interest and achievements in healthy eating among caterers. The organisers were surprised with the number of entries and the range of establishments already active. The winner in 1986 was the Civil Service Catering Organisation of the Welsh Office and the Swan restaurant in Knutsford, Cheshire. Three of the other entries are printed below to show the wide range of establishments now practising healthy catering and imagination in their menus.

Sodexho Scotland Offshore feed the workers on oil-rigs in the North Sea – demanding work and demanding customers because as one of the judges,

Miriam Polunin, said, '[the workers] . . . probably give rather too much consideration to food because other entertainments are limited by the situation, and [they] have a lifestyle which includes a considerable amount of physical (weather, flying) and emotional (family separation) stress.' Their dinner menu is everything but dull and is clearly described.

SEDEXHO SCOTLAND OFFSHORE FULMAR ALPHA

DINNER MENU

Prawn Mangetout and Hazelnut Salad
Fresh pink prawns, mangetout and lemon juice served with a black pepper and hazelnut dressing

Yogurt Gazpacho Soup
Tomatoes, cucumber, green pepper, fennel and mint finely chopped and laced with yoghurt and lemon juice

Steamed Sole in Chinese Leaves and Herb Sauce
Lemon sole fillets wrapped in Chinese leaves and poached over a fish stock, served with a herb sauce consisting of pepper, tarragon, chervil, chives and parsley

Grilled Lamb Cutlets with Aniseed and Orange Sauce
Lamb cutlets marinaded in aniseed and orange juice cooked and served with a reduced marinade sauce and garnished with orange segments

Moroccan Chicken Cous-Cous
Poached skinned chicken joints served with a tomato, courgette and chervil sauce on a bed of cous-cous

Devilled Rump Steak
Sauted prime rump steak with Dijon mustard, English mustard, cayenne pepper and a thin sauce of red wine and Worcestershire sauce served with a green salad

Baked Potatoes and Savoury Fillings/Ratatouille of Vegetables
New Boiled Potatoes with Mint Sauce/Sultana Pilaff
Savoury brown rice and sultanas cooked in stock

Collation of Green Salad plus
Celery and Orange Salad and Yoghurt Coleslaw with Raisins

Assorted Cold Sweets – Baked Russet Apples

Selection of Wholemeal Breads and Rolls

The Wildfowl Trust at Slimbridge in Gloucestershire is not the place to expect a good meal, much less a healthy one, going on experiences of facilities offered generally for day-trippers. The refurbished restaurant, however, offered a refurbished menu that would be proudly presented anywhere. In fact the offer of roast chicken may be happier almost anywhere but a Wildfowl Trust.

SLIMBRIDGE WILDFOWL TRUST

MENU

Various Home-made Soups with Granary Bread
Fresh Melon

Jacket Potatoes – plain or with cheese

Cauliflower Cheese

Vegetarian Lasagne

Fresh Trout baked with Herbs

Roast Chicken

Selection of Fresh Vegetables and Stir-fry

Assorted Salads with Home Baked and Roasted Meats

Fresh Fruit Salad

Assorted Sandwiches in Granary Bread

Cheese and Biscuits

Assorted Filled French Sticks

Home-made Biscuits and Cakes (no artificial colours)

Assorted Beverages including:
decaffeinated coffee
fresh fruit juices
alcohol-free beer
mineral water

Institutional caterers do not have a good reputation for food. Hospitals are not often congratulated on the quality of their catering and the long-stay hospitals like those for the elderly and mentally-ill are often the least well resourced. However the Dingleton Hospital covered by the Scottish Borders Health Board is a mental hospital standing up for the interest and skills of Health Service caterers with their Italian menu.

DINGLETON HOSPITAL MENU

A TASTE OF ITALY

LUNCH

Minestrone Soup

Wholemeal Spaghetti Bolognaise

Stuffed Green Lasagne

Antipasti of Stuffed Peppers

Roman Style Stuffed Tomatoes

Baked Potatoes

Bean and Tuna Fish Antipasti

Fresh Fruit Salad

Ginger and Raisin Yoghurt Ice Cream

Italian Cheese and Biscuits

SUPPER

Plate size Sardine Pizza

Tagliatelli with Ham and Tomato

Wheatmeal Macaroni Gratin

Ratatouille

Cherry and Orange Yoghurt Ice Cream

Open Apricot Pie

MAKE MENUS INFORMATIVE

Every menu is an opportunity to communicate with customers. Make sure the essential details of dishes being offered and prices are clear but don't stop there.

Describe dishes with sufficient detail so that customers know the important ingredients and cooking methods used. Indicate particularly low-calorie or low-fat and -sugar foods. Don't worry about giving the exact measures of calories or ingredients. A simple code or symbol is easier to understand and gives the same message. Indicate new dishes specially chosen for health and pleasure and put a note at the bottom of the menu explaining your interest in both the enjoyment and consequent health of your customers. Some caterers are even putting healthy eating tips on the backs of menus.

CONSULT THE CUSTOMERS

Most caterers assert that they can provide only what their customers want; but how do they consult? It is not enough to look at popularity of dishes on menus. It is well known that, within limits, the British will eat whatever is placed before them. Eating the food provided doesn't mean satisfaction, especially in a works canteen in the middle of an isolated industrial estate where alternatives are as scarce as unsweetened baked beans. Go one better. Involve customers by announcing new dishes and asking for comments. Simple surveys can be conducted by leaving short questionnaires on tables or having them presented to customers by waiters. Attitudes to healthy eating, past menus and new dishes or other changes can all be gleaned with an added benefit – customers will appreciate being consulted and will be impressed by caterers taking such interest in their customers' health. Good consultations will make customers more aware of the caterer's role and will help increase status.

Surveys can also measure how much customers know about healthy eating and this information could inspire some appropriate ways of helping customers learn while they eat. This has been explored in many places in school dining rooms and within the Health Service where health promotion is a major function. These resources are available to any caterers.

TRAINING AND BACKUP

Caterers and their staff will be better able to make the change to healthy catering with some training. The more the principles are understood, the more they can see why it is a good change, and the more they can see how the changes can be made practical in terms of their jobs, the easier it will be to introduce healthy catering and the greater the chances of success. Training does not require days or weeks away at college and need not be expensive.

There is an increasing number of one- or two-day intensive workshops available. These are ideal for caterers or chefs who can learn the principles and be able to train other staff back on the job. It is also possible to arrange for short sessions in the workplace. These can involve all staff and are an economical option and many people can get trained at once. Consult the local Health Authority to see if they can help with training. Organisations like the Vegetarian Society and the London Food Commission, as well as a number of Food and Health consultants, can help with advice and a range of training packages.

Unfortunately few of the professional catering training courses offer adequate healthy catering content so young caterers are still entering the profession without either an awareness of healthy eating principles or the skills to practise. This is an important reason why some caterers dismiss the merits of healthy catering. All caterers need to become aware of the new evidence supporting healthy eating among doctors and nutritionists and respond to the rapidly increasing awareness of the public. Caterers should turn these changed attitudes to food into a new opportunity and they should invite local training colleges to review their courses in the interests of future graduates. Practising caterers could explore the availability of in-service training and also invite their colleges to explore all opportunities.

CHARITY BEGINS AT HOME

Most caterers eat their work, so to speak. If the British diet is as bad as the scientists say, caterers are not exempt from the dangers. If the fact that catering meals are, on average, among the most unhealthy is to be believed, caterers have special reasons to change their own eating habits. Take care to interest staff in their own health and make sure that their meals can be as healthy as those offered customers. This will not only make for healthier staff but also help motivate them to care for the customers.

CHAPTER SIX

MARKETING
HEALTHY EATING

*"The destiny of nations
depends on the manner
wherein they take their
food."*
BRILLAT SAVARIN

When caterers promote their skills the public listens. What do Anton
Mosimann, *nouvelle cuisine*, Sarah Brown and MacDonalds have in
common? The simple answer is that they are well known to the public. All
are the subject of well organised marketing campaigns. Ask the next person
you set eyes on to list another four well known names in the world of
catering and watch the hesitation, even if they happen to be a caterer.
Caterers don't do enough to market their skills and wares. In truth, very few
caterers do anything at all about selling themselves, even in their own
workplaces. Appetite is a powerful force, but there are better ways of
pulling customers.

   Healthy catering is a classic case for successful marketing. There is plenty
of evidence that the public want better food, and more caterers are taking up
healthy catering. The customer interest and the product are there but they
are rarely introduced. Marketing is the key and it does two important
things; it gives customers the information about what you are doing through
advertising and it draws customers into your own establishment through
promotions.

   Marketing embraces everything the caterer does, and many things not
done. It includes advertising, promotions and public relations but do not
think that is enough. A successful advertising campaign could have
customers queuing at opening time but if there is no provision for nursing
mothers, no wheel-chair access, or the toilets are down a dark and damp
alley out the back, the customers' interest in returning could wane speedily.

   Marketing is for caterers as much as for the manufacturers of soap
powders and Rolls Royce cars. Too many caterers say they are reluctant to
move into healthy catering because they fear either that their customers will

eat only what they are used to seeing on menus or that introducing healthy dishes is risky because the customers may not like the 'new food'. However, as evidenced up and down the land, these fears are a mixture of myth and ignorance of the facts in the trade.

British eating patterns may be conservative by European standards, but eaters are becoming much more adventurous, even more curious to explore new foods. Supermarket shelves are the clearest sign of this change, but the restaurant, take-away and even industrial catering sectors are having to make changes to keep up with customer interests. Look at the industrial caterers' recipes in this book to see what is now being served in workplaces! Where is the evidence that 'new foods' will be shunned? Where is the evidence that customers will not like healthy catering? All evidence seems to go the other way. There is real ignorance of what the public would like and how they feel about healthy catering. Part of the reason is that nobody has asked, perhaps because nobody has seen the need. Chapter 1 discussed how caterers and the public have kept apart, meeting only through the medium of waiter or counter staff. The result is that caterers know little of their customers and customers know still less about caterers. What a little marketing could do!

Marketing is still an isolated activity in the industry, but every caterer has much to gain from a little indulgence. For the profit sector, more custom means higher turnover and potential for higher profits. The institutional or cost sector can expect a higher uptake which reduces unit costs and may justify greater investment in capital equipment or staff training. Both sectors stand to gain much in professional status. Marketing is not expensive; it costs what you are prepared or able to invest and many useful activities are cheap or free. But remember that successful marketing should pay for itself. The key to success is a little aforethought and some careful planning.

BE CLEAR ABOUT OBJECTIVES

Time and resources are scarce so decide what you want to achieve before you choose the marketing strategy or the marketing activities. Objectives might be:

● To increase existing customers' knowledge of healthy eating.

● To increase the uptake of your healthy dishes or your special healthy *table d'hôte* menu.

● To increase the average number of mid-day meals eaten in your workplace canteen from 2 a week per worker to 4 a week.

- To increase the number of customers by 20 per cent over the summer.

- To increase customer awareness of caterers' skills and caring for customers' health.

- To have customers see eating in your establishment as a contribution to a healthier lifestyle.

CHOOSE THE TARGET

The most important customers are those you already have. This is especially true when healthy catering is being introduced. Care should be given to keeping them informed, making them feel they are the object of your efforts and, where possible, involving them in your own decisions about menus and any health or nutrition information.

New customers are a different target and matter as much to institutional caterers as to the profit sector. A restaurant or works canteen could want simply to increase total custom or perhaps aim at an identified sector of potential customers now taking pub lunches instead of eating in the workplace restaurant. A school meals service could be aiming at children bringing packed lunches and be trying to increase meal uptake from say 30 per cent to 60 per cent of children.

Once the target is identified, marketing strategies can be decided.

WHAT'S THE MESSAGE?

Healthy caterers have no shortage of subject matter to market. Decide what you have which you feel would interest customers.

- Protect your heart and general health with my menus!

- Calorie conscious? Try our weight maintenance menus.

- New healthy menus with traditional foods modified for health and special new dishes.

- A new menu system with a special healthy option indicated for each course.

- Healthy eating information for customers and every dish marked to show important nutritional features like calories, salt, etc.

- Cheapest healthy food in town.

- The healthiest bangers and beans around.

- Take-home recipe cards of favourite dishes.

- A new customer consultation where the chefs discuss the food and ask for menu suggestions.

MARKETING ACTIVITIES

The most obvious is *advertising* which is used to create a greater public awareness about either your establishment's existence or what it offers. The scale may be national, regional or as local as a high-street or workplace noticeboard. Big budgets allow for the expense of TV advertising but the medium used and the scale must match the subject. There would be little benefit in advertising a single restaurant in Southend or a Birmingham factory restaurant on TV. However, it could be different when advertised on workplace noticeboards, in the works newsletter, and on a leaflet in every paypacket.

Very cheap advertising is available through leaflets, and through both local radio and local newspapers which are a foolproof way of reaching local target groups. Colourful posters about healthy eating or drawing attention to advantages of eating your healthy foods can combine low-key education messages with advertising on restaurant walls.

Direct mail can be very effective as it reaches only the chosen audience and there is little wastage. Restaurants could mail existing customers very effectively and workplaces usually have access to the internal mail or pay-slip envelopes to reach every employee.

Promotions can be very productive. They include anything which aims to create greater interest in the establishment or its menus, and are often designed specifically to get customers sitting at tables or trying particular parts of menus.

Promotions are an excellent way of getting existing customers interested in your new healthy menus, trying new dishes, using new health information messages and, through it all, learning more about your skills and activities on their behalf.

Special promotions could include:

- Healthy eating days where the entire menu is healthy with specially informative leaflets describing each dish and its nutritional merits placed on tables.

● Invite a local celebrity with a positive health image to cook or help serve food on a healthy eating theme day with the local dietitian on hand to answer any general questions about healthy food.

● Have special Country Cooking days where healthy national dishes are offered together with recipes to take home.

● Set out a salad table; arrange a business lunch or slimmers' day where leaflets on how to eat well on a business lunch without threatening health or how to maintain desirable weight without unhealthy 'crash diets'.

● Organise a competition to guess the amount of fat or sugar in various dishes over a week. This makes customers realise that any of your dishes can be 'healthy' and helps them understand the care you have taken in preparing their food. Have the dietitians analyse the food and make a presentation of a suitable healthy prize – like free meals for a fortnight in your own place!

● When a favourite cookery writer of yours produces another *healthy* cookbook, announce a day when customers can get a copy signed at their table by the author. The better known the writer, the more your own work will be associated with theirs. This one is very possible to arrange; publishers are happy to have author signings especially if enough people will see the event, and you can have the local press involved (again through the publisher's good offices) to maximise publicity for yourself and the new book.

● Invite customers or local celebrities to cook their favourite dish one day. This works well in the workplace where the MD or the front of house receptionist could be equally a draw so long as they have interesting dishes to offer. Restaurants in the commercial sector could invite someone from a TV food programme or the local Mayor to do the honours.

There is no shortage of promotional ideas around. They don't have to be unique to work for you, they have only to work. Uniqueness does help get publicity in advance, though, and might be a consideration if you wanted good press coverage. Think what would interest your customers, choose a promotion that is both feasible (but don't be put off just because something *sounds* impossible) and that you can afford. Many promotions in the list above are free. Remember that there are many other people interested in promoting healthy eating and you can team up. Local Health Authority dietitians and health promotion staff are skilled at such promotions and will be delighted to help. Local Authorities as well as Health Authorities often have food and health policies operating and therefore have both a special interest and the resources to help you promote better eating.

Promotions can be successful in any type of establishment – from a hospital staff dining room through the local pub to the Dorchester. The only limitations are imagination and thoughtful planning.

PUBLIC RELATIONS AND THE MEDIA

Public relations (PR) is about communications and everyone does it already, though not often consciously and not always with the desired results. Public relations includes communications with customers, your professional colleagues, the food trade, health workers, the public and the media. Like it or not, PR does much to determine your image and hence how customers and potential customers see your establishment. Of course chance is not a good servant and it may not convey your chosen image to the world. Don't leave it to chance; spend time and energy planning your image and use the tools of PR to communicate it.

Caterers, like most people, tend either to forget about using PR or to feel that it is only for exhibitionists. Both are mistakes for healthy caterers. PR can help bring in customers and is a powerful way of conveying your image as an informed, caring and effective provider of enjoyable, healthy foods.

Good PR begins with simple steps which are appropriate to any type of establishment. Think first of how you see yourself and how you want your customers to see both you and your food. Assess how you are seen to see how your image of your own establishment matches that of the outside world. There may already be differences you might decide to correct – perhaps you are a good healthy vegetarian restaurant but are seen as a faddist, or have been converting all your hospital menus to healthier designs for the last year but your customers think all your food comes in from an external kitchen on a new cook-chill system and they haven't noticed any difference! Try to understand the reasons and plan a PR campaign to shift opinions your way. PR is about positive communications and is good business, whatever your business.

Simple PR begins with:

● Well informed staff who are willing to explain your new menus and know why they are healthier.

● Always inviting your customers' views on the menu, especially on new dishes.

• Make a point of being seen in the dining areas, converse with customers and don't only ask about your food. This applies to restaurants as much as to school meals and hospitals. The PR task is the same and the rewards as great.

• Whenever you change the menu, introduce new dishes or start putting nutritional information on menus and noticeboards, make it clear that you are following your customers' interests which you gathered through listening and talking with them.

• Take an interest in local conferences or any committees discussing healthy eating. Join any you think relevant and you can make the time for. Form a group of local caterers interested in health for joint PR as well as for getting good advice and support. All such activity will enhance the public's appreciation of your work.

• Don't just consult your customers, tell the customers that you have and give them the results on the menu, the restaurant wall or noticeboard, or through the local media.

• Get in the local press and on local radio or TV as often as possible. Any coverage is good coverage (with the odd exception like having a summons following a visit from the local Environmental Health Officer).

BEFRIEND A JOURNALIST

Outside of your own place of work, the media are your best friend in PR. Media includes broadcast (radio and TV) and printed media (newspapers, magazines). Good press relations are free publicity and good PR. Do not see the press as enemies who appear only to criticise. This view is very widespread and leads to a fear which is both false and deprives the holder of enjoyable and profitable publicity. Many otherwise enthusiasts are put off using the media for fear of being misquoted or quoted out of context. This can happen, but when it does it is most often because the journalists were not given enough information when they needed it or it wasn't clear enough.

There are two points about journalists which you should have firmly imprinted in both your consciousness and your memory. They will affect forever and significantly your attitude to this important marketing and PR tool.

FIRST, news is made; it doesn't happen. Whatever the events, they only become news when, and if, a journalist decides to put it in the paper or news bulletin. Not many people read more than one newspaper, but spend big tomorrow and buy one of each national daily. Compare the front pages and see how they have chosen totally different stories to be the news that day. The inside pages are usually more different.

SECOND, journalists are usually harassed people, trying to cover too many stories on most of which they are neither experts nor have enough information at hand to make a good story. Often, their life is the worse because they don't have enough ideas to produce the number of stories demanded by their even more harassed editor. In short, they are very nice people trying to do a job and are very appreciative of all the help they can get.

The starting position therefore is to realise that journalists are friends in need and that YOU can help them create the news. All of the following advice should be taken up:

● Befriend a suitable journalist on the local papers and radio. Make a calculated choice. There is no point getting the racing correspondent who would have no time for your stories and may not even like the food or health writer. Go for the health or social services correspondents, or the editor of the features or women's pages. Another ploy is to choose the journalist whose name appears over stories you like on food or health features. Phone them and invite them for a meal, preferably when you have your first story ready for them.

The purposes in befriending are many and are valuable. A personal contact is better than an anonymous contact for a start, but you can build a relationship where they beg to come to you personally for advice, tips, or as the 'local expert' on healthy catering which means you keep getting quoted.

● Keep yourself informed of what is in the media (for that is where many journalists get their stories!) and what is happening in catering and health. Offer yourself as a source of advice. Be helpful to journalists and suggest they contact you whenever they want some help. Make yourself indispensable. It may take some time, but journalists are busy people too and appreciate you putting yourself out, especially to help them.

● Let them know your news. Make sure that the story is likely to interest them as they will get fed up with a continuing supply of stories they can't ever use and will lose faith in you before the big story arrives. Better to give too few good stories than many bad ones which end up in the bin. Decide whether you have a news item or whether it might be better on the features pages, then go to the appropriate journalist. Local radio and TV are always looking for local news items and ideas for their magazine programmes; these are very popular with broadcasters and are made up of large numbers of short items often strung together with music in between. *Woman's Hour* or *You and Yours* on Radio 4 are good examples, but all local radio and TV stations have their own versions.

If in doubt, ask a journalist what stories they want.

● Issue PRESS RELEASES to let the journalists know first your news, and second, how *you* want it told. A press release is carefully written to appeal to journalists. It should have a heading which clearly and briefly gives the story. The title should be eye-catching as journalists see hundreds of these each and every day and mediocrity is deadly – straight to the bin. The first sentence should state the story and give WHAT, WHO, WHERE, WHY as briefly as possible. Following paragraphs then fill out each of the points, but again as briefly as possible. A good press release is written so that a journalist can take the copy and insert it as it is into the paper or news bulletin. Of course your release may be modified, even shortened, but the better it is, the less change will happen. You can therefore make the news!

Writing press releases is an art, but it is easy to learn and a friendly journalist will be only too pleased to advise. After all, you are helping them do their own job. Much can be learned by studying news stories in the paper or magazine you are aiming the press release at; you can learn the style, and see how information is ordered with the important points in the first sentence or paragraph and the information getting less necessary as the eye reads down the story.

● Aim for the big time. Do not ignore the national papers or TV and radio. Your story could be of as much interest there as in your high street, but remember they usually have much more to choose from so send only your hot stories. Magazine programmes on all channels and on BBC radio search all the time for good local stories with a difference. It is also a good bet that whenever you make it on the national media, the local press will be around like bees to nectar.

● Use the letters columns of papers and magazines. You can raise issues relevant to stories in the media and get both your own point of view and sometimes timely publicity. One well known food campaigner used always to make a point of getting a letter in the national paper read by the government minister on the same mornings of all meetings with ministers or their civil servants.

Letters should be brief. Try to make the letter relevant to something which has just appeared which also means that you shouldn't delay in writing. Always telephone the letters editor to say you have a letter on the way. Deliver it by hand if possible; you will be the first letter on the subject the editor sees and will have it there closer to the date of the original item.

Be hospitable. Invite journalists round for a meal. They all appreciate a treat and it gives a good opportunity for you to get acquainted and to explain your work and interests in a relaxed way. Don't wait until you have a story either, arrange a time which is mutually convenient.

Marketing your skills will not only help your business, it will help more of your customers, and customers-to-be, to follow the same healthier lifestyle you are promoting. You will be satisfied and can take satisfaction in helping make for a healthier population.

RECIPES FOR HEALTH

INTRODUCTION

Recipes from the standard repertoire rarely fit happily on healthy menus without careful selection or significant modification. It is likely that any collection would contain some examples which could satisfy the basic healthy criteria set out in the first part of this book, but they are difficult to identify without a detailed nutritional analysis of ingredients. Nor is it common practice to print nutritional information alongside recipes to help caterers choose healthy recipes to suit their menus, or customers' special needs.

Of course caterers can conduct their own nutritional analyses, but how much easier if analyses were necessary only to check modifications to a standard recipe or to assess a caterer's own creations. All recipes in this book have been chosen because they fit the healthy criteria discussed in earlier chapters and each recipe is presented with a table showing its nutritional analysis.

SOURCE OF RECIPES

During all my work with caterers, especially in the National Health Service and schools, I have been struck by the initiative and dedication of caterers who have overcome their limited resources to produce meals which satisfy their customers and protect health as well. To show what is being achieved, I organised a national call for healthy recipes by advertising in the *Hospital Caterer* and the *Caterer and Hotelkeeper* magazines and by distributing leaflets. Recipes came from hotels, restaurants, schools, hospitals, industrial caterers, and even a North Sea oil rig. The best recipes received make up this collection. They illustrate the imagination of the profession and the ease with which healthy catering can be enjoyable eating. Each recipe carries the name of its contributor and a full address list is found in Appendix VIII.

NUTRITIONAL ANALYSIS

Each recipe was computer analysed by Wendy Doyle at the Nuffield Institute of Comparative Medicine in London. Their system is based on the

McCance and Widdowson tables called *The Composition of Foods*, with some additional information also available to the computer. The kind of nutritional information given for each recipe is shown in the table below:

NUTRIENT ANALYSIS PER PORTION			
	kcal	kJ	MINERALS &
ENERGY (CALORIES)	120	502	VITAMINS IN
	GRAMS	AS % TOTAL	LARGE
	(g)	ENERGY	AMOUNTS
TOTAL FAT	5.7	43.0	Potassium,
SATURATED FAT	1.9	8.2	calcium,
TOTAL CARBOHYDRATE	15.0	48.0	iron, zinc
ADDED SUGARS	1.8	5.6	Vitamins
PROTEIN	2.7	8.9	A, B group,
			C, folic acid

Energy is presented in the familiar units of calories (kcal) as well as kilo Joules which are the standard metric units. Convert from kcal to kilo Joules by multiplying by 4.184 (1 kcal = 4.184 kJ).

Fats, carbohydrates and protein have been presented in two forms. First, as a simple weight in grams in one portion of each recipe and second, each is converted into energy equivalents and expressed as a percentage of the total energy (or calories) in a portion. Note that only the percentages for TOTAL FAT, TOTAL CARBOHYDRATE and PROTEIN should be added to make up the whole, or 100 per cent. The amounts of saturated fat and added sugars are included in the TOTAL FAT and TOTAL CARBOHYDRATE values.

Minerals and vitamins are listed only when they are present in what I have called arbitrarily a 'large amount'. The purpose is to indicate those recipes which are good sources of particular nutrients which is a useful guide to mixing foods in meals and menus to give a wide range of nutrients. For those nutrients listed in the UK tables of Recommended Daily Allowances of Nutrients (Appendix III), I have listed nutrients for which a serving from the recipe supplies ⅕ (20 per cent) of the RDA or more. For nutrients not included in the UK RDAs, I used the USA Recommended Daily Amounts which, while generally higher than those for the UK, give a useful guide. For potassium, I used a ¹⁄₁₀th of the estimated average daily intake which is normally in excess of a healthy body's needs. Nutrients like phosphorus and magnesium which are widely available in foods and for which dietary problems are rare were not considered for inclusion in the tables.

USING THE NUTRITIONAL INFORMATION

To say a recipe supplies a large amount of a nutrient is not to say it should be the only source of that nutrient eaten during a day. Remember that a meal usually consists of more than one dish or food and that an individual may eat from three to 10 meals each day, especially considering the trend to more snack meals. Be careful of taking single values from the percentage of total energy column in isolation. This column does not show how much of each source of energy is present; it shows only the *proportion of the total energy* supplied from each source of energy. For example a dish could be very low in fat and calories and yet show that fat supplies perhaps more than half of the energy. How? Look at the recipe for trout and almonds on p. 120. It contains only fresh trout, almonds, pistachios and some mushrooms, but it has 55 per cent of its energy from fat and yet supplies only 260 calories a portion. The percentage of energy from fat is high because, with very little carbohydrate supplying energy, the only other source of energy is protein which gives 40 per cent. But the amount of fat is not high and it is low in saturates, helping to make this dish a very popular healthy choice on menus.

A recipe providing a high percentage of energy from fat could be combined on menus with accompanying dishes which offer a low percentage of calories from fat values. In this way the proportion of energy from fat can be brought down to the level of 30 per cent recommended in the NACNE guidelines.

VEGETARIAN AND VEGAN SYMBOLS

Vegetarian recipes carry a V for vegetarian symbol against the title. Vegan recipes are marked Vg. The definitions of vegetarian and vegan used are on pp. 31–33. In allocating the symbol I have been strict. Recipes specifying only 'polyunsaturated margarine' have not been labelled vegetarian because some polyunsaturated margarines contain fish or animal fats and oils. However many such recipes could be made for vegetarians so long as care was taken to ensure that *all ingredients* satisfied the criteria.

SALT

Few recipes include salt. Even when the original included salt, this was deleted on the principle that customers should be left to add their own salt at the table. Caterers should use their own judgement on whether to add salt to their cooking, and how much. It may be helpful to begin by reducing the salt slowly over several months. Research shows that tastes adapt to this slow reduction and your regular customers will not notice the reduction. A notice explaining this to customers will help them appreciate your interest in their wellbeing and may also encourage less salt to be used at the table.

STARTERS

GRAPEFRUIT & AVOCADO MAYONNAISE (V)

Stuart Cabeldu Catering Ltd
London

10 portions		25 portions
	Mayonnaise	
¹/₂ tsp	SUGAR	1 tsp
³/₄ tsp	DRY MUSTARD	2 tsp
	CAYENNE PEPPER	
4 tsp	WHITE WINE VINEGAR OR LEMON JUICE	10 tsp
2	EGG WHITES	4
8 fl oz (250 ml)	SUNFLOWER OIL	1 pt (570 ml)
	SHREDDED LETTUCE FOR SERVING	
2–3	AVOCADO, PEELED, SLICED AND DIPPED IN LEMON JUICE	6
2–3	GRAPEFRUIT, PEELED AND SEGMENTED	6

1 Make the mayonnaise by mixing sugar, seasonings and vinegar in a bowl. Whisk egg whites until thick but not stiff then add half the oil, slowly beating the while. Continue beating while adding the seasonings and vinegar mixture. Add the remaining oil and vinegar slowly while beating. Chill before using.
2 Place lettuce in individual serving bowls.
3 Mix avocado and grapefruit and place on lettuce. Top with mayonnaise.

An alternative is to blend avocado and grapefruit to a smooth paste for use as a dip with crudités.

NUTRIENT ANALYSIS PER PORTION			
	kcal	kJ	MINERALS & VITAMINS IN
ENERGY (CALORIES)	340	1421	LARGE
	GRAMS (g)	AS % TOTAL ENERGY	AMOUNTS
TOTAL FAT	35.0	93.0	Potassium
SATURATED FAT	4.9	13.0	Vitamins
TOTAL CARBOHYDRATE	3.0	3.3	C, E
ADDED SUGARS	.3	.3	
PROTEIN	3.3	3.9	
FIBRE	1.3g		
SALT	60.9mg		

MIAMI COCKTAIL (V,VG)

Compass
London

10 portions		25 portions
3	ORANGES	8
3	GRAPEFRUIT	8
1	MELON, LARGE	2

1 Wash and dry oranges and grapefruit. Peel and separate segments and remove their membranes.
2 Cut melon in half and scoop out balls of fruit.
3 Distribute fruit evenly among individual serving dishes. Chill before serving.

NUTRIENT ANALYSIS PER PORTION			
	kcal	kJ	MINERALS &
ENERGY (CALORIES)	53	230	VITAMINS IN
	GRAMS	AS % TOTAL	LARGE
	(g)	ENERGY	AMOUNTS
TOTAL FAT	–	–	Potassium
SATURATED FAT	–	–	Vitamin
TOTAL CARBOHYDRATE	13.0	90.0	C
ADDED SUGARS	–	–	
PROTEIN	1.5	11.0	
FIBRE	2.3g		
SALT	.78g		

STUFFED AVOCADO PEARS I
(V, VG)
Graham Scholey
Watford

10 portions		25 portions
5	AVOCADOS	13
2 oz (60 g)	SHALLOTS	5 oz (140 g)
1 oz (30 g)	POLYUNSATURATED VEGETABLE MARGARINE	2 oz (60 g)
10 oz (285 g)	BUTTON MUSHROOMS	3 lb (1.35 kg)
1 oz (30 g)	BREADCRUMBS	5 oz (140 g)
1 oz (30 g)	CHOPPED ALMONDS	3 oz (90 g)
	Sauce	
1½ oz (45 g)	CORNFLOUR	4 oz (115 g)
1 pt (570 ml)	WATER	2½ pt (1.5 l)
2 tbsp	TOMATO PURÉE	4 oz (115 g)
2 tbsp	SOYA SAUCE	2 fl oz (50 ml)
1 dash	WORCESTERSHIRE SAUCE	3 or 4 dashes

1 Finely chop shallots and sweat for 2–3 min. in the margarine.

2 Chop mushrooms and add to the shallots. Cook out and allow juices to evaporate.

3 Halve avocados lengthways. Scoop out flesh and sieve or blend until smooth. Keep skins. Add breadcrumbs, shallots and mushroom mixture to avocado and mix. Pipe into reserved skins, sprinkle almonds on top.

4 Mix cornflour in 2 cups of water. Mix together rest of sauce ingredients and boil. Whisk in cornflour mixture and simmer until clear.

5 Heat stuffed avocados in oven or brown under a grill. Serve hot with sauce.

NUTRIENT ANALYSIS PER PORTION			
	kcal	kJ	MINERALS & VITAMINS IN LARGE AMOUNTS
ENERGY (CALORIES)	318	1329	
	GRAMS (g)	AS % TOTAL ENERGY	
TOTAL FAT	29.0	81.0	Potassium,
SATURATED FAT	3.5	9.9	iron, copper
TOTAL CARBOHYDRATE	9.1	11.0	Vitamins
ADDED SUGARS	–	–	B_6, C, E,
PROTEIN	6.5	8.1	folic acid
FIBRE	3.8g		
SALT	.18g		

STUFFED AVOCADO PEARS II *(V)*

Shirlee Posner
London

10 portions		25 portions
3	MEDIUM ORANGES	7
4 oz (115 g)	LIGHT TAHINI	10 oz (285 g)
10 oz (285 g)	GREEK YOGHURT	25 oz (750 g)
5	RIPE AVOCADOS	13
5	CELERY STALKS (CHOPPED)	2 heads
2 bnch	WATERCRESS	5 bnch
2 oz (60 g)	TOASTED SUNFLOWER SEEDS	6 oz (170 g)

1 Peel oranges, separate into segments and slice thinly. Place in large mixing bowl.

2 Mix tahini and yoghurt. Pour over oranges.

3 Halve avocados lengthways. Spoon flesh out with a teaspoon (larger spoonsful will break up in mixing) and combine with orange mixture. Reserve skins intact. Add celery.

4 Toss lightly and spoon back into avocado skins. Garnish with watercress and toasted sunflower seeds.

NUTRIENT ANALYSIS PER PORTION			
	kcal	kJ	MINERALS &
ENERGY (CALORIES)	396	1695	VITAMINS IN
	GRAMS	AS % TOTAL	LARGE
	(g)	ENERGY	AMOUNTS
TOTAL FAT	35.0	80.0	Potassium,
SATURATED FAT	5.7	13.0	calcium, iron
TOTAL CARBOHYDRATE	11.0	10.0	Vitamins
ADDED SUGARS	–	–	B_6, C, E,
PROTEIN	10.0	10.0	folic acid
FIBRE	4.4g		
SALT	96.5mg		

MINTED COUS-COUS
FILLED TOMATOES *(V,VG)*

Linda Lennison
Cheshire

10 portions		25 portions
10	MEDIUM FIRM TOMATOES	25
1 tbsp	SUNFLOWER OIL	2 tbsp
5 oz (140 g)	COUS-COUS	13 oz (375 g)
1 heaped tsp	MINT SAUCE	2–3 heaped tsp
	LETTUCE, WATERCRESS AND LEMON FOR GARNISH	

1 Boil a kettle of water.

2 Cut the tomatoes into water-lily shapes (or simply cut off the top third) and scoop out the seeds.

3 Heat sunflower oil in a thick bottomed pan, add cous-cous and stir continuously for one minute.

4 With pan still on heat, add about 2 fl oz (50 ml) of hot water while stirring, allowing the cous-cous to cook in the steam. Continue adding small quantities of water and stirring until the cous-cous is soft and fluffy – 3 to 5 minutes.

5 Add mint sauce and mix into the cous-cous.

6 Fill tomatoes with mixture and either microwave on low for 1 minute, or place in the bottom of a warm oven for 10 minutes to heat through just before serving.

7 Serve on a bed of lettuce garnished with watercress and a slice of lemon.

Useful as a starter or a vegetable.

NUTRIENT ANALYSIS PER PORTION			
	kcal	kJ	MINERALS & VITAMINS IN LARGE AMOUNTS
ENERGY (CALORIES)	59	247	
	GRAMS (g)	AS % TOTAL ENERGY	
TOTAL FAT	2.1	33.0	Vitamins
SATURATED FAT	.3	5.0	C, E
TOTAL CARBOHYDRATE	9.1	58.0	
ADDED SUGARS	–	–	
PROTEIN	1.4	9.6	
FIBRE	1.0g		
SALT	5.3mg		

PEARS WITH CHEESE DRESSING *(V)*

Linda Lennison
Cheshire

10 portions		25 portions
5	LARGE PEARS	13
1	CLOVE GARLIC	1
8 oz (225 g)	SKIMMED MILK CHEESE	1 lb 4 oz (565 g)
2 tsp	WINE VINEGAR	3 tsp
2 tsp	LEMON JUICE	4 tsp
	BLACK PEPPER	
	LETTUCE	
	WATERCRESS FOR GARNISH	

1 Halve, peel and core pears and dip in lemon juice to prevent browning.

2 Cut garlic clove and rub round a small mixing bowl.

3 Add the cheese, vinegar, lemon juice, and black pepper to taste then mix well to the consistency of whipped cream. If mixture is too dry, mix in a little sunflower oil.

4 Place pear halves into separate serving dishes on a bed of lettuce and top with the dressing.

5 Garnish with watercress and serve chilled.

NUTRIENT ANALYSIS PER PORTION			
	kcal	kJ	MINERALS &
ENERGY (CALORIES)	31	130	VITAMINS IN
	GRAMS	AS % TOTAL	LARGE
	(g)	ENERGY	AMOUNTS
TOTAL FAT	.1	2.6	None
SATURATED FAT	.1	1.5	
TOTAL CARBOHYDRATE	4.7	57.0	
ADDED SUGARS	–	–	
PROTEIN	3.2	42.0	
FIBRE	1.0g		
SALT	.25g		

LIVER & LENTIL PÂTÉ

Mary Deans
Edinburgh

10 portions		25 portions
4 oz (115 g)	POLYUNSATURATED MARGARINE	10 oz (285 g)
2 cloves	GARLIC, CRUSHED	5
2	ONIONS, DICED	5
1 lb (450 g)	CHICKEN LIVERS	2½ lb (1.1 kg)
½ lb (225 g)	BROWN LENTILS	1¼ lb (565 g)
	PEPPER	
	LEMON JUICE	
10	SLICES WHOLEMEAL TOAST	25
	Garnish	
1	LETTUCE	2
3	TOMATOES	8
1 punnet	CRESS	2 punnets

1 Melt margarine in pan. Add garlic, onion and livers at low heat. Cook for 10–20 minutes, stirring frequently.

2 Boil lentils for 30 minutes or until just soft. Drain.

3 Mix liver and lentils and blend smooth. Add seasoning and lemon juice to taste.

4 Transfer to serving bowls and refrigerate covered to set.

5 Garnish and serve with hot toast.

NUTRIENT ANALYSIS PER PORTION			
	kcal	kJ	MINERALS & VITAMINS IN
ENERGY (CALORIES)	327	1367	LARGE AMOUNTS
	GRAMS (g)	AS % TOTAL ENERGY	
TOTAL FAT	14.0	38.0	Potassium,
SATURATED FAT	2.87	7.9	iron, copper
TOTAL CARBOHYDRATE	34.0	39.0	zinc
ADDED SUGARS	–	–	Vitamins A,
PROTEIN	19.0	23.0	B group,
FIBRE	7.7g		C, D,
SALT	1.0g		folic acid

LENTIL PÂTÉ I *(V,VG)*

East West Restaurant
London

10 portions		25 portions
10½ oz (300 g)	BROWN LENTILS	1 lb 10 oz (750 g)
²/₃ oz (20 g)	AGAR AGAR	1²/₃ oz (50 g)
8 oz (225 g)	ONIONS, DICED	20 oz (565 g)
2	CLOVES OF GARLIC	4
8 oz (225 g)	CARROTS, DICED	20 oz (565 g)
	SOYA OIL	
½ oz (15 g)	FRESH BASIL, CHOPPED FINELY	1 oz (30 g)
	NUTMEG TO TASTE	
	SHOYU, TO TASTE	
²/₃ oz (20 g)	GREEN NORI FLAKES	1²/₃ oz (50 g)

1 Cover lentils with water, mix agar agar to a smooth paste with a little water then add to lentils and boil until cooked.

2 Sauté onions, garlic and carrots in a small amount of soya oil until cooked. Add lentils, basil and grated nutmeg. Season with shoyu.

3 Line a bread tin with green nori (pre-soaked until soft), fill it with lentil mixture, cover with more nori and chill to set.

4 Tip from tin onto serving plate and serve with toast or good wholemeal rolls.

Nori is a form of sea weed available from wholefood suppliers.

NUTRIENT ANALYSIS PER PORTION			
	kcal	kJ	MINERALS & VITAMINS IN LARGE AMOUNTS
ENERGY (CALORIES)	105	439	
	GRAMS (g)	AS % TOTAL ENERGY	
TOTAL FAT	.4	3.8	Potassium
SATURATED FAT	.1	.5	Vitamin A
TOTAL CARBOHYDRATE	19.0	67.0	
ADDED SUGARS	–	–	
PROTEIN	7.6	29.0	
FIBRE	4.6g		
SALT	121mg		

LENTIL PÂTÉ II *(V, VG)*

Pauline Moore
Douglas
Isle of Man

10 portions		25 portions
4 tbsp	SUNFLOWER OIL	10 tbsp
2	ONIONS, SLICED	5
1 lb (450 g)	MUSHROOMS, SLICED	2½ lb (1.1 kg)
4 tbsp	TAHINI	10 tbsp
4 tsp	YEAST EXTRACT	10 tsp
1 lb (450 g)	COOKED BROWN LENTILS	2½ lb (1.1 kg)
4 tbsp	CHOPPED PARSLEY	10 tbsp
1 oz (30 g)	SESAME SEEDS	2 oz (60 g)

1 Sweat onions in the oil then chop and add mushrooms.
2 Combine tahini, yeast extract, lentils and parsley. Add onions and mushrooms. The mixture should be thick and smooth.
3 Turn into a bowl. Decorate with sesame seeds and chill.
4 Serve with wedges of rye toast.

NUTRIENT ANALYSIS PER PORTION			
	kcal	kJ	MINERALS & VITAMINS IN LARGE AMOUNTS
ENERGY (CALORIES)	219	915	
	GRAMS (g)	AS % TOTAL ENERGY	
TOTAL FAT	16.0	67.0	Potassium,
SATURATED FAT	2.2	9.1	calcium, iron
TOTAL CARBOHYDRATE	12.0	20.0	Vitamins
ADDED SUGARS	–	–	B_2, C, E,
PROTEIN	8.2	15.0	nicotinic acid
FIBRE	4.1g		
SALT	.29g		

MUSHROOM & HERB PÂTÉ
(V, VG)

Shirlee Posner
London

10 portions		25 portions
8 oz (225 g)	POLYUNSATURATED PURE VEGETABLE MARGARINE	1 lb 4 oz (565 g)
2	CLOVES GARLIC	4
1 lb 8 oz (675 g)	ONION, FINELY CHOPPED	3 lb (1.35 kg)
½ oz (15 g)	MIXED/PROVENÇAL HERBS, DRIED	1 oz (30 g)
1 lb 4 oz (550 g)	MUSHROOMS, BUTTONS OR CUPS	3 lb (1.35 kg)
4 oz (115 g)	WHOLEMEAL BREADCRUMBS	10 oz (285 g)

1 Melt margarine in pan and add onions, garlic and herbs. Chop mushrooms finely and add, cooking until soft.

2 Mix in breadcrumbs and chill well to set before serving with slices of tomato and wholemeal rolls.

Cashew nuts, walnuts or celery with red wine can be added for a richer pâté.

NUTRIENT ANALYSIS PER PORTION			
	kcal	kJ	MINERALS & VITAMINS IN LARGE AMOUNTS
ENERGY (CALORIES)	214	895	
	GRAMS (g)	AS % TOTAL ENERGY	
TOTAL FAT	19.0	80.0	Potassium,
SATURATED FAT	3.3	14.0	copper
TOTAL CARBOHYDRATE	8.5	15.0	Vitamins
ADDED SUGARS	–	–	A, C, E
PROTEIN	2.7	5.1	
FIBRE	3.4g		
SALT	.65g		

TOFU MOUSSE *(V, VG)*

East West Restaurant
London

10 portions		25 portions
2¼ lb (1 kg)	CARROTS	5½ lb (2½ kg)
2¼ lb (1 kg)	TOFU CURD	5½ lb (2½ kg)
1 tbsp	SHOYU	2 tbsp
5½ oz (150 g)	UMEBOSHI PLUMS	12½ oz (370 g)
¾ oz (20 g)	FRESH BASIL	1¾ oz (50 g)
	CUCUMBER SLICES FOR GARNISH	

1 Slice carrots and boil in a little water until soft.

2 Blend carrots and other ingredients together. Pour into greased flan dishes or individual ramekins. Bake in moderate oven 350°F (180°C, gas mark 4) for 30 minutes and allow to cool in dishes.

3 The mousse may be turned out of dishes or left in for serving. Decorate with cucumber slices.

4 It can be glazed with agar agar jelly. Dissolve 1 tbsp of powdered agar agar in 1 pint (570 ml) of boiling water, add shoyu to taste, and allow to cool until just starting to set; then glaze tofu and allow to set in cool place.

Umeboshi plums are pickled oriental plums which can be used to flavour dishes like this or eaten on their own.

NUTRIENT ANALYSIS PER PORTION			
	kcal	kJ	MINERALS &
ENERGY (CALORIES)	109	456	VITAMINS IN
	GRAMS (g)	AS % TOTAL ENERGY	LARGE AMOUNTS
TOTAL FAT	4.2	35.0	Potassium,
SATURATED FAT	.6	5.1	calcium,
TOTAL CARBOHYDRATE	9.9	34.0	iron, zinc,
ADDED SUGARS	.83	2.8	Vitamins
PROTEIN	8.4	31.0	A, B₆, C
FIBRE	4.3g		
SALT	.25g		

SAINT TROPEZ *(V,VG)*

Jean-Claude Juston
London

10 portions		25 portions
3 lb (1.35 kg)	STONEGROUND STRONG, WHOLEMEAL FLOUR	7½ lb (3.45 kg)
4 oz (115 g)	FRESH YEAST	10 oz (285 g)
5–6 pt (2.8–3.4 l)	TEPID WATER	14–16 pt (7.7–9.0 l)
5	GREEN PEPPERS	13
5	RED PEPPERS	13
1 lb (450 g)	MUSHROOMS	2½ lb (1.1 kg)
1 lb (450 g)	BANANAS	2½ lb (1.1 kg)
1 lb (450 g)	GRAPES	2½ lb (1.1 kg)
8 oz (225 g)	WALNUTS	1½ lb (675 g)

1 Make bread dough which should not be sticky. Roll into a square about ½ in (1.5 cm) thick.

2 Chop vegetables, fruit and nuts and mix. Dampen dough and spread a layer of mixture over whole surface.

3 Roll square from one side into a French stick. Slice into ½ in (1.5 cm) circles and arrange on a greased baking sheet.

4 Bake at 400°F (200°C, gas mark 6) for 20 minutes. Serve hot with pesto sauce, or cold with humus or pâté.

This dish makes an excellent starter or snack. It was named after a visit to the Picasso Museum in Saint Tropez where the artist's palettes were reminiscent of the dish.

NUTRIENT ANALYSIS PER PORTION			
	kcal	kJ	MINERALS & VITAMINS IN LARGE AMOUNTS
ENERGY (CALORIES)	635	2654	
	GRAMS (g)	AS % TOTAL ENERGY	
TOTAL FAT	15.0	22.0	Potassium,
SATURATED FAT	1.8	2.5	iron, zinc
TOTAL CARBOHYDRATE	107.0	63.0	Vitamins
ADDED SUGARS	–	–	B_6, C, E,
PROTEIN	24.0	15.0	nicotinic acid,
FIBRE	19.0g		folic acid
SALT	35.6mg		

SOUPS

MINESTRONE SOUP
Compass
London

10 portions		25 portions
2 tbsp	SOYA OIL	5 tbsp
1 lb (450 g)	ONION, CHOPPED	2 lb 8 oz (1.1 kg)
	GARLIC CLOVES, TO TASTE	
8 oz (225 g)	CARROTS	1 lb 12 oz (565 g)
4 oz (115 g)	CELERY, SLICED THINLY	10½ oz (300 g)
12 oz (350 g)	POTATOES, DICED	2 lb (900 g)
1 lb (450 g)	CANNED TOMATOES	2 lb 8 oz (1.1 kg)
3 pt (1.7 l)	BEEF STOCK	7 pt 10 fl oz (4.25 l)
	BOUQUET GARNI	
5 oz (140 g)	WHOLEMEAL MACARONI	12 oz (350 g)
12 oz (350 g)	CANNED BUTTERBEANS	2 lb (900 g)
4 tbsp	PARSLEY, CHOPPED	10 tbsp
	PEPPER TO TASTE	

1 Fry off onion and garlic. Add carrots, celery, potatoes and tomatoes. Pour in stock and bouquet garni.

2 Boil, covered, for 30 minutes. Add macaroni and beans then return to boil until macaroni is soft. Stir in parsley and serve.

NUTRIENT ANALYSIS PER PORTION			
	kcal	kJ	MINERALS & VITAMINS IN LARGE AMOUNTS
ENERGY (CALORIES)	337	1409	
	GRAMS (g)	AS % TOTAL ENERGY	
TOTAL FAT	5.4	14.0	Potassium,
SATURATED FAT	1.0	2.7	iron, zinc
TOTAL CARBOHYDRATE	62.0	69.0	Vitamins
ADDED SUGARS	–	–	A, B_1, B_6,
PROTEIN	14.0	17.0	nicotinic acid,
FIBRE	13.0g		C, E, folic acid
SALT	1.62g		

TOMATO SURPRISE SOUP
(V , VG)

Compass
London

10 portions		25 portions
3½ oz (105 g)	BROAD BEANS	9 oz (255 g)
3½ oz (105 g)	RUNNER BEANS, CHOPPED	9 oz (255 g)
7 oz (200 g)	ONION, CHOPPED	1 lb 2 oz (510 g)
3 pt (1.7 l)	VEGETABLE STOCK	7 pt 10 fl oz (5.25 l)
1 lb 5 oz (590 g)	KIDNEY BEANS, CANNED	3 lb 8 oz (430 g)
6 oz (170 g)	WHOLEMEAL PASTA, COOKED AND DRAINED	15 oz (430 g)
4 tsp	TOMATO PURÉE	10 tsp
2 tbsp	PARSLEY, CHOPPED	5 tbsp

1 Cook broad beans, runner beans, onions in stock for 10 minutes in covered pan.

2 Add kidney beans, pasta and tomato purée. Boil for 13 minutes or until pasta is tender. Garnish with parsley.

NUTRIENT ANALYSIS PER PORTION			
	kcal	kJ	MINERALS &
ENERGY (CALORIES)	212	886	VITAMINS IN
	GRAMS	AS % TOTAL	LARGE
	(g)	ENERGY	AMOUNTS
TOTAL FAT	1.3	5.4	Potassium,
SATURATED FAT	.1	.5	calcium, iron,
TOTAL CARBOHYDRATE	34.0	59.0	zinc
ADDED SUGARS	–	–	Vitamins
PROTEIN	19.0	35.0	B_1, B_6, C,
FIBRE	17.0g		folic acid
SALT	1.22g		

CARROT & ORANGE SOUP

Mary Deans
Edinburgh

10 portions		25 portions
2	LARGE ONIONS, DICED	5
2	LEEKS, SLICED FINELY	5
2 lb (900 g)	CARROTS, DICED	5 lb (2.3 kg)
3 oz (90 g)	POLYUNSATURATED MARGARINE	8 oz (225 g)
3 pt (1.75 l)	SKIMMED CHICKEN STOCK	7 pt (3.95 l)
2	ORANGES, ZEST AND JUICE	5
	PEPPER	

1 Sauté onions, leek and carrot in margarine until starting to brown.
2 Add stock, orange juice and zest, bring to boil and simmer 45 minutes.
3 Liquidise, adding more water if necessary for consistency. Season as necessary.
4 Serve hot.

NUTRIENT ANALYSIS PER PORTION			
	kcal	kJ	MINERALS &
ENERGY (CALORIES)	116	485	VITAMINS IN
	GRAMS	AS % TOTAL	LARGE
	(g)	ENERGY	AMOUNTS
TOTAL FAT	7.4	58.0	Vitamins
SATURATED FAT	1.42	11.0	A, C
TOTAL CARBOHYDRATE	11.0	35.0	
ADDED SUGARS	–	–	
PROTEIN	2.2	7.7	
FIBRE	4.3g		
SALT	.81g		

CARROT SOUP

Rhonda Roberts
Auchenblae, Scotland

10 portions		25 portions
3	ONIONS	6
2	LEEKS	6
2	CLOVES GARLIC, CRUSHED	5
¹/₂ oz (15 g)	SAFFLOWER OIL	2 oz (60 g)
2 lb (900 g)	CARROTS	6 lb (2.7 kg)
¹/₂ lb (225 g)	CANNED TOMATOES	1 lb (450 g)
4¹/₂ pt (2.35 l)	CHICKEN STOCK	12 pt (6.75 l)

1 Chop onion and leek finely.

2 Sweat onion, leek, garlic in the oil in a saucepan.

3 Grate carrot and add to the saucepan. Continue on low heat for 5 minutes.

4 Add tomatoes and stock. Bring to boil then simmer for 10 minutes. Cool and liquidise.

5 Serve hot with a small wholemeal roll.

NUTRIENT ANALYSIS PER PORTION			
	kcal	kJ	MINERALS & VITAMINS IN LARGE AMOUNTS
ENERGY (CALORIES)	54	226	
	GRAMS (g)	AS % TOTAL ENERGY	
TOTAL FAT	1.6	27.0	Vitamins
SATURATED FAT	.3	4.8	A, C
TOTAL CARBOHYDRATE	7.9	55.0	
ADDED SUGARS	–	–	
PROTEIN	2.3	17.0	
FIBRE	4.1g		
SALT	.67g		

CHICKEN & SWEETCORN SOUP

Pauline Moore
Douglas
Isle of Man

10 portions		25 portions
2	ONIONS, CHOPPED	5
1 oz (30 g)	POLYUNSATURATED MARGARINE	2½ oz (75 g)
1 tsp	POWDERED GINGER	2½ tsp
1 tsp	HOT PEPPER SAUCE	2½ tsp
1 lb (450 g)	COOKED CHICKEN, DICED	2½ lb (1.1 kg)
1 lb (450 g)	TINNED SWEETCORN	2½ lb (1.1 kg)
4 pt (2.25 l)	VEGETABLE OR CHICKEN STOCK	10 pt (5.6 l)
2 tbsp	LEMON JUICE	5 tbsp

1 Sweat onions in margarine.
2 Add ginger and pepper sauce.
3 Stir in chicken followed by sweetcorn.
4 Add stock and lemon juice and bring to the boil.
5 Serve hot with bread rolls.

NUTRIENT ANALYSIS PER PORTION

	kcal	kJ	MINERALS & VITAMINS IN LARGE AMOUNTS
ENERGY (CALORIES)	189	790	
	GRAMS (g)	AS % TOTAL ENERGY	
TOTAL FAT	9.0	43.0	Potassium,
SATURATED FAT	2.5	12.0	zinc,
TOTAL CARBOHYDRATE	11.0	21.0	nicotinic acid
ADDED SUGARS	3.4	6.8	Vitamin C
PROTEIN	17.0	36.0	
FIBRE	2.9g		
SALT	2.3g		

Opposite: *Minestrone Soup p. 108, Cod Wellington p. 126.*
Over: *Lentil Pâté p. 104, Miami Cocktail p. 97, Saint Tropez p. 107.*

LEEK & CARROT SOUP *(V,VG)*
Mary Morgan
Leicester

10 portions		25 portions
1 lb (450 g)	CARROTS, DICED	2 lb 8 oz (1.12 kg)
1 lb (450 g)	LEEKS, WASHED AND SLICED	2 lb 8 oz (1.12 kg)
2 oz (60 g)	POLYUNSATURATED VEGETABLE MARGARINE	10 oz (285 g)
2.5 pt (1.5 l)	VEGETABLE STOCK	6.5 pt (3.65 l)
2	BAY LEAVES	4
¼ oz (8 g)	NUTMEG OR PAPRIKA	½ oz (15 g)
	PEPPER TO TASTE	

1 Sauté vegetables in the margarine until cooked but not browned.
2 Add stock and bay leaves. Simmer for 20 minutes or until vegetables are soft.
3 Remove bay leaves and liquidise until smooth. Season to taste.
4 Serve in warmed bowls. Garnish with grated carrot and blanched julienne of leek and a sprinkling of nutmeg or paprika.

This basic recipe for a smooth soup can be used for any combination of vegetables and fruits. It could be garnished also with a whirl of Greek yoghurt.

NUTRIENT ANALYSIS PER PORTION			
ENERGY (CALORIES)	kcal 86	kJ 359	MINERALS & VITAMINS IN LARGE AMOUNTS
	GRAMS (g)	AS % TOTAL ENERGY	
TOTAL FAT	4.9	51.0	Potassium
SATURATED FAT	.9	9.2	Vitamins
TOTAL CARBOHYDRATE	6.2	27.0	A, C, E
ADDED SUGARS	–	–	
PROTEIN	4.5	21.0	
FIBRE	2.7g		
SALT	1.2g		

Previous Page: *Baked Rainbow Trout with Almonds and Pistachios p. 120.*
Opposite: *Grilled Seafood Kebab with Sautéd Beansprouts p. 122.*

SALADS

CELERY, APPLE & SESAME SALAD I *(V)*

Elsbeth Japp
Aberdeen

10 portions		25 portions
2	HEADS CELERY	4
6	RED DESSERT APPLES	15
2 lb (900 g)	LOW FAT NATURAL YOGHURT	5 lb (2.25 kg)
2 tbsp	SESAME SEEDS, ROASTED	4 tbsp

1 Chop celery and apples finely.
2 Place celery and apple in salad bowl and toss in the yoghurt.
3 Sprinkle with sesame seeds and serve.

NUTRIENT ANALYSIS PER PORTION			
	kcal	kJ	MINERALS & VITAMINS IN LARGE AMOUNTS
ENERGY (CALORIES)	90	376	
	GRAMS (g)	AS % TOTAL ENERGY	
TOTAL FAT	1.7	17.0	Potassium,
SATURATED FAT	.64	6.4	calcium
TOTAL CARBOHYDRATE	14.0	58.0	Vitamin C
ADDED SUGARS	–	–	
PROTEIN	6.1	27.0	
FIBRE	3.5g		
SALT	.67g		

CELERY, APPLE & SESAME SALAD II *(V,VG)*

Linda Lennison
Cheshire

10 portions		25 portions
2	EATING APPLES	5
1 dsp	LEMON JUICE	2 dsp
3 dsp	SUNFLOWER OIL	6 dsp
few drops	SESAME OIL	1 tsp
1/2	HEAD CELERY	1
1 tbsp	SESAME SEEDS	2 tbsp

1 Peel, core and chop the apples.
2 Place the apple in a salad bowl and toss in lemon juice.
3 Add the oils and toss again.
4 Chop the celery and mix it, and the seeds into the apple.

NUTRIENT ANALYSIS PER PORTION			
	kcal	kJ	MINERALS &
ENERGY (CALORIES)	47	196	VITAMINS IN
	GRAMS	AS % TOTAL	LARGE
	(g)	ENERGY	AMOUNTS
TOTAL FAT	3.9	74.0	Vitamin E
SATURATED FAT	.5	9.8	
TOTAL CARBOHYDRATE	2.8	22.0	
ADDED SUGARS	–	–	
PROTEIN	.6	5.3	
FIBRE	1.0g		
SALT	.14g		

CUCUMBER & SWEET PEPPER SALAD *(V,VG)*

East West Restaurant
London

10 portions		25 portions
2¼ lb (1 kg)	TOFU CURD	5½ lb (2.5 kg)
10½ oz (300 g)	MISO	1 lb 10 oz (735 g)
4	MEDIUM CUCUMBERS	10
2¼ lb (1 kg)	RED AND GREEN PEPPERS	5½ lb (2.5 kg)
7 oz (200 g)	ONIONS	1 lb 2 oz (510 g)
7 fl oz (200 ml)	SHOYU	17½ fl oz (500 ml)
4 fl oz (100 ml)	RICE VINEGAR	10 fl oz (300 ml)
8½ oz (250 g)	OLIVES	1 lb 6 oz (620 g)

1 Slice tofu into thick slices and marinade in miso dissolved in a pint (600 ml) of water for at least 2 hours, preferably a day.
2 Dice cucumbers, cut peppers, remove tofu from miso (which can be reused) and cut into small pieces (about ¼ inch cubes), dice onions.

3 Mix all ingredients carefully in a salad bowl, sprinkle in the olives and toss in the rice vinegar.

NUTRIENT ANALYSIS PER PORTION			
	kcal	kJ	MINERALS &
ENERGY (CALORIES)	212	886	VITAMINS IN
	GRAMS	AS % TOTAL	LARGE
	(g)	ENERGY	AMOUNTS
TOTAL FAT	9.3	40.0	Potassium,
SATURATED FAT	1.4	5.9	calcium,
TOTAL CARBOHYDRATE	18.0	32.0	iron, zinc
ADDED SUGARS	–	–	Vitamins
PROTEIN	15.0	29.0	B$_1$, B$_6$, C,
FIBRE	2.0g		nicotinic acid
SALT	1.53g		folic acid

CHICKEN & TARRAGON SALAD

Leith's Good Food
London

10 portions		25 portions
2 × 4 lb (1.8 kg)	CHICKEN, COOKED	4 × 5 lb (9.2 kg)
10 fl oz (300 ml)	YOGHURT	1 pt 5 oz (700 ml)
2 tbsp	FRESH TARRAGON, CHOPPED	5 tbsp
4	SPRING ONIONS, CHOPPED	10
4 oz (115 g)	GRAPES, SEEDED	8 oz (225 g)

1 Skin and carve chicken. Arrange in two rows in large plate.
2 Mix yoghurt, tarragon and onions. Spoon between rows of chicken. Garnish with grapes.

NUTRIENT ANALYSIS PER PORTION			
	kcal	kJ	MINERALS &
ENERGY (CALORIES)	238	995	VITAMINS IN
	GRAMS	AS % TOTAL	LARGE
	(g)	ENERGY	AMOUNTS
TOTAL FAT	8.1	31.0	Potassium,
SATURATED FAT	2.6	10.0	calcium
TOTAL CARBOHYDRATE	4.1	6.5	Vitamin B$_6$,
ADDED SUGARS	–	–	nicotinic acid
PROTEIN	37.0	63.0	
FIBRE	.3g		
SALT	.36g		

GREEN & ARAME SALAD
(V , V G)

East West Restaurant
London

10 portions		25 portions
2¼ lb (1 kg)	LEAF GREENS	5½ lb (2.5 kg)
2 oz (60 g)	ARAME	5 oz (140 g)
7 fl oz (200 ml)	APPLE JUICE	17½ fl oz (545 ml)
4 fl oz (100 ml)	SHOYU	10 fl oz (300 ml)
2¼ lb (1 kg)	SATSUMAS OR TANGERINES	5½ lb (2.5 kg)

1 Cut greens into strips and blanch.
2 Soak the arame for a few minutes then boil for 10–15 minutes in the apple juice, shoyu and a little water. Drain.
3 Peel fruits and cut segments into thirds. Mix with greens and arame and serve.

Arame is a shredded seaweed from Japan. It is brown and has a delicate sweetish taste and is a good source of calcium.

NUTRIENT ANALYSIS PER PORTION			
	kcal	kJ	MINERALS &
ENERGY (CALORIES)	70	293	VITAMINS IN
	GRAMS (g)	AS % TOTAL ENERGY	LARGE AMOUNTS
TOTAL FAT	.9	12.0	Potassium,
SATURATED FAT	.1	.7	calcium,
TOTAL CARBOHYDRATE	13.0	70.0	iron
ADDED SUGARS	–	–	Vitamins
PROTEIN	3.3	19.0	A, C, E,
FIBRE	2.1g		folic acid
SALT	.23g		

CARROT, PARSNIP & NUT SALAD (V)

Linda Lennison
Cheshire

10 portions		25 portions
½ lb (225 g)	CARROTS	1½ lb (675 g)
½ lb (225 g)	PARSNIPS	1 lb (450 g)
1 oz (30 g)	NUTS CHOPPED	2–3 oz (60–90 g)
5 oz (140 g)	LOW-FAT NATURAL YOGHURT	10 oz (285 g)
	FRESH GROUND BLACK PEPPER	

1 Roughly shred carrots and parsnips.
2 Mix all ingredients, adding black pepper to taste.

NUTRIENT ANALYSIS PER PORTION			
ENERGY (CALORIES)	kcal 41	kJ 171	MINERALS & VITAMINS IN LARGE AMOUNTS
	GRAMS (g)	AS % TOTAL ENERGY	
TOTAL FAT	1.6	36.0	Vitamin A
SATURATED FAT	.4	8.1	
TOTAL CARBOHYDRATE	4.9	45.0	
ADDED SUGARS	–	–	
PROTEIN	2.0	19.0	
FIBRE	1.8g		
SALT	91.4mg		

CUCUMBER & BANANA SALAD (V)

Linda Lennison
Cheshire

10 portions		25 portions
1	LARGE BANANA	2
1 dsp	LEMON JUICE	2 dsp
3 oz (90 g)	LOW-FAT NATURAL YOGHURT	5 oz (140 g)
½	CRISP LETTUCE (COS OR WEBBS)	1
⅓	CUCUMBER	1

1 Peel and slice bananas and toss gently in lemon juice.
2 Add yoghurt and mix well.
3 Shred lettuce finely and dice cucumber then add both to the mixture and toss carefully.

NUTRIENT ANALYSIS PER PORTION			
ENERGY (CALORIES)	kcal 20	kJ 84	MINERALS & VITAMINS IN
	GRAMS (g)	AS % TOTAL ENERGY	LARGE AMOUNTS
TOTAL FAT	.2	9.3	None
SATURATED FAT	.1	4.1	
TOTAL CARBOHYDRATE	3.9	73.0	
ADDED SUGARS	–	–	
PROTEIN	.9	18.0	
FIBRE	.8g		
SALT	30.5mg		

BARLEY & FRUIT SALAD
(V, VG)
Linda Lennison
Cheshire

10 portions		25 portions
12 oz (350 g)	PEARL BARLEY, COOKED	2 lb (900 g)
4 fl oz (100 ml)	FRESH ORANGE JUICE	12 fl oz (350 ml)
2 oz (60 g)	MIXED RAISINS, SULTANAS	5 oz (140 g)

1 While the barley is still hot, add the orange juice and vine fruits. Stir well.
2 Leave until cool and serve.

This is a quick and easy salad which is inexpensive and very popular in my Macclesfield restaurant.

NUTRIENT ANALYSIS PER PORTION			
ENERGY (CALORIES)	kcal 44	kJ 184	MINERALS & VITAMINS IN
	GRAMS (g)	AS % TOTAL ENERGY	LARGE AMOUNTS
TOTAL FAT	.1	2.6	None
SATURATED FAT	.1	.6	
TOTAL CARBOHYDRATE	11.0	91.0	
ADDED SUGARS	–	–	
PROTEIN	.7	6.3	
FIBRE	.9g		
SALT	8.9mg		

FRESH FISH

BAKED RAINBOW TROUT WITH ALMONDS & PISTACHIOS

Chester Boyd Ltd
London

10 portions		25 portions
10	*TROUT FILLETS*	25
	SOYA OIL, FOR GREASING	
4 oz (115 g)	*FLAKED ALMONDS, TOASTED*	*10 oz (285 g)*
4 oz (115 g)	*PISTACHIO NUTS*	*10 oz (285 g)*
4 oz (115 g)	*MUSHROOMS, SLICED*	*10 oz (285 g)*
2	*SMALL HANDSFUL FRESH HERBS, CHOPPED*	5
	WHITE WINE AND LEMON JUICE TO ANOINT	

1 For each fillet, cut a heart-shaped piece of grease-proofed paper 1½ times the length of the fillet. Fold in half down the midline, crease and open out again.

2 Singe skin side of each fillet in a hot pan with a wipe of oil. Oil papers and place fillets on one side of crease. Add almonds, pistachios, mushroom and herbs with a dash of wine and lemon juice.

3 Bake on a sheet at 350°F (180°C, gas mark 4) for 10–15 minutes. Serve in paper.

NUTRIENT ANALYSIS PER PORTION			
	kcal	kJ	MINERALS & VITAMINS IN LARGE AMOUNTS
ENERGY (CALORIES)	260	1087	
	GRAMS (g)	AS % TOTAL ENERGY	
TOTAL FAT	16.0	55.0	Potassium,
SATURATED FAT	2.2	7.6	iron
TOTAL CARBOHYDRATE	3.1	4.5	Vitamins E,
ADDED SUGARS	–	–	nicotinic acid
PROTEIN	26.0	40.0	
FIBRE	2.3g		
SALT	.21g		

MACKEREL WITH YOGHURT STUFFING

Stuart Cabeldu Catering Ltd
London

10 portions		25 portions
10	SMALL MACKEREL, CLEANED	25
	BLACK PEPPER	
	LITTLE SUNFLOWER OIL	
3	SMALL ONIONS, CHOPPED	7
1/2	HEAD CELERY, CHOPPED	1
9 oz (255 g)	LOW-FAT PLAIN YOGHURT	24 oz (675 g)
5 oz (140 g)	EDAM, GRATED	12 oz (350 g)
5 oz (140 g)	WHOLEWHEAT BREADCRUMBS	12 oz (350 g)
2½ tsp	LEMON JUICE	6 tsp
	PARSLEY FOR GARNISH	

1 Sprinkle inside fish with pepper.
2 Sweat onion and celery in oil until soft.
3 Mix yoghurt, cheese, breadcrumbs, lemon and the onion mixture. Divide between fish and stuff in gut cavity. Secure opening with skewers or toothpicks. Bake at 350°F (180°C , gas mark 4) for 20–25 mins. Garnish with parsley.

NUTRIENT ANALYSIS PER PORTION			
	kcal	kJ	MINERALS &
ENERGY (CALORIES)	614	2567	VITAMINS IN
	GRAMS (g)	AS % TOTAL ENERGY	LARGE AMOUNTS
TOTAL FAT	41.0	61.0	Potassium,
SATURATED FAT	10.9	16.0	calcium,
TOTAL CARBOHYDRATE	10	6.4	iron, zinc
ADDED SUGARS	–	–	Vitamins A,
PROTEIN	50.0	33.0	B group,
FIBRE	2.5g		C, D, E
SALT	1.49g		

GRILLED SEAFOOD KEBAB WITH SAUTÉD BEANSPROUTS

John McManus
London

10 portions		25 portions
1¼ lb (565 g)	RED MULLET	3 lb 2 oz (1.41 kg)
1 lb 14 oz (860 g)	DOVER SOLE	4 lb 11 oz (2.1 kg)
10	LANGOUSTINE	25
1¼ lb (565 g)	MONKFISH	3 lb 2 oz (1.47 kg)
1	SMALL PIECE FRESH GINGER ROOT	2
3	CLOVES GARLIC	5
1¼ lb (565 g)	BEANSPROUTS	3 lb (1.35 kg)
	SOY SAUCE	
	CORIANDER LEAVES, CHOPPED FOR GARNISH	

1 Cut red mullet into pieces. Fillet the sole, cut each one lengthwise in two or three pieces and tie each piece into a knot. Peel the langoustine. Bone the monkfish and cut in chunks.

2 Place fish on a skewer, season and mark on a hot charcoal grill (make sure grill is clean). Place in oven at 400°F (200°C, gas mark 6) for 4–5 minutes.

3 Peel and finely chop ginger and garlic. Sauté quickly the beansprouts in a hot pan (their moisture will keep them from burning). While sprouts still crisp, add ginger, garlic and soy sauce.

4 Lie beansprouts on a serving dish and carefully remove fish from skewer and arrange on top of sprouts. Garnish with a sprinkle of coriander leaves.

NUTRIENT ANALYSIS PER PORTION			
	kcal	kJ	MINERALS & VITAMINS IN LARGE AMOUNTS
ENERGY (CALORIES)	281	1175	
	GRAMS (g)	AS % TOTAL ENERGY	
TOTAL FAT	8.1	26.0	Potassium,
SATURATED FAT	1.3	4.0	iron, zinc
TOTAL CARBOHYDRATE	3.6	4.8	Vitamins
ADDED SUGARS	–	–	B_1, B_{12},
PROTEIN	48.0	68.0	nicotinic acid,
FIBRE	.3g		C, D
SALT	.83g		

COD IN CIDER (or Apple Juice)
Linda Lennison
Cheshire

10 portions		25 portions
1	SMALL ONION	*2 large*
1 dsp	SUNFLOWER OIL	*2 dsp*
6 oz (170 g)	MUSHROOMS	*1 lb (450 g)*
10	COD FILLETS	*25*
	FLOUR FOR DUSTING	
	BLACK PEPPER	
16 fl oz (½ l)	DRY CIDER OR APPLE JUICE	*1 l*

1 Slice the onions and fry them in the oil.

2 Chop the mushrooms and add them to the onions. Fry for a few minutes longer.

3 Flour and season the fish and spread them out in an oven-proof dish. Cover with the onions and mushrooms.

4 Heat the cider in a saucepan until boiling and pour over the fish. Cook in a preheated oven 350°F (180°C, gas mark 4) for 20 minutes.

5 Serve hot with the sauce poured over the fish. (Sauce may be thickened with cornflour.)

NUTRIENT ANALYSIS PER PORTION			
	kcal	kJ	MINERALS &
ENERGY (CALORIES)	207	865	VITAMINS IN
	GRAMS	AS % TOTAL	LARGE
	(g)	ENERGY	AMOUNTS
TOTAL FAT	2.7	12.0	Potassium
SATURATED FAT	.5	2.0	Vitamins
TOTAL CARBOHYDRATE	1.9	3.4	B_6, B_{12},
ADDED SUGARS	–	–	nicotinic acid
PROTEIN	40.0	78.0	
FIBRE	.6g		
SALT	.46g		

HADDOCK WITH
PINEAPPLE & LIME

Linda Lennison
Cheshire

10 portions		25 portions
10	UNSMOKED HADDOCK FILLETS	25
	BLACK PEPPER	
	FLOUR FOR DUSTING	
2	LIMES	5
16 fl oz (½ l)	PINEAPPLE JUICE	1¾ pt (1 l)
1 tsp	FENNEL SEED	2 tsp

1 Season and flour fillets then lay them in one layer in an oven-proof dish.

2 Put lime juice plus zest together with pineapple juice in saucepan and heat to boiling. Pour over fish.

3 Cook in middle of a preheated oven 350°F (180°C, gas mark 4) for 20–30 minutes.

4 Serve hot with sauce poured over fish (sauce may be thickened with a cornflour if preferred), and garnished with fennel seeds.

This dish freezes well. Any white fish can be substituted for haddock.

NUTRIENT ANALYSIS PER PORTION			
	kcal	kJ	MINERALS &
ENERGY (CALORIES)	197	823	VITAMINS IN
	GRAMS	AS % TOTAL	LARGE
	(g)	ENERGY	AMOUNTS
TOTAL FAT	1.4	6.5	Potassium
SATURATED FAT	.3	1.2	Vitamins
TOTAL CARBOHYDRATE	7.2	14.0	B_6, B_{12},
ADDED SUGARS	2.5	4.7	nicotinic acid,
PROTEIN	39.0	79.0	C
FIBRE	.7g		
SALT	.7g		

HOME-MADE FISH CAKES
Chris Gray
Southsea

10 portions		25 portions
1½ lb (675 g)	WHITE FISH, e.g. COD	4¾ lb (2.1 kg)
	BAY LEAF, PARSLEY STALKS, PEPPER	
3	EGGS, SEPARATED	7
1½ lb (675 g)	POTATOES, COOKED AND MASHED	4¾ lb (2.1 kg)
12 oz (350 g)	CHEDDAR CHEESE, GRATED	2 lb (900 g)
1 oz (30 g)	WHOLEMEAL FLOUR	2½ oz (75 g)
5 oz (140 g)	WHOLEMEAL BREADCRUMBS	12½ oz (365 g)

1 Poach fish in a shallow pan with bay leaf, parsley and pepper for 10 minutes. Drain. Flake fish, discarding skin and bones.

2 Add egg yolks to mashed potato and mix in fish and cheese.

3 With floured hands, shape mixture into fish cakes. Beat the egg whites. Dip fish cakes into egg whites and roll in breadcrumbs. Cakes should be chilled for at least 30 minutes before cooking.

4 Grill on a rack for ten minutes, turning once.

NUTRIENT ANALYSIS PER PORTION			
	kcal	kJ	MINERALS & VITAMINS IN LARGE AMOUNTS
ENERGY (CALORIES)	303	1267	
	GRAMS (g)	AS % TOTAL ENERGY	
TOTAL FAT	14.0	41.0	Potassium, zinc
SATURATED FAT	8.1	24.0	
TOTAL CARBOHYDRATE	21.0	26.0	Vitamins A,
ADDED SUGARS	–	–	B_2, B_6, B_{12}, C
PROTEIN	25.0	33.0	
FIBRE	2.2g		
SALT	.91g		

COD WELLINGTON

Burley Manor Hotel & Restaurant
Burley

10 portions		25 portions
5 lb (2.3 kg)	SPINACH	*12½ lb (5.7 kg)*
2 lb (900 g)	MUSHROOMS	*5 lb (2.3 kg)*
4 lb (1.8 kg)	TOMATOES	*10 lb (4.5 kg)*
4	CLOVES GARLIC	*10*
5 lb (2.3 kg)	COD FILLET	*12½ lb (5.7 kg)*
1	BOX FILO PASTRY	*2½*
1	BUNCH DILL	*2½*

1 Shred and poach spinach.

2 Chop mushrooms and mix in spinach.

3 Blanch, peel and de-seed tomatoes. Liquidise with garlic. Heat in a saucepan.

4 Divide cod into portions, steam and allow to cool. Place portions on a sheet of filo folded in half, top with spinach mixture and bake at 375°F (190°C, gas mark 5) for 10 minutes.

5 Place hot tomato sauce on serving plate, place cod parcel on top and cut in half to display fish. Garnish with dill.

NUTRIENT ANALYSIS PER PORTION			
	kcal	kJ	MINERALS &
ENERGY (CALORIES)	334	1396	VITAMINS IN
	GRAMS	AS % TOTAL	LARGE
	(g)	ENERGY	AMOUNTS
TOTAL FAT	4.5	12.0	Potassium,
SATURATED FAT	.8	2.1	calcium,
TOTAL CARBOHYDRATE	26.0	29.0	iron, zinc
ADDED SUGARS	.6	.6	Vitamins A,
PROTEIN	49.0	59.0	B group,
FIBRE	6.9g		C, E,
SALT	1.34g		folic acid

FISH FLORENTINE

Compass
London

10 portions		25 portions
1 lb 4 oz (565 g)	SPINACH, FROZEN	3 lb (1.35 kg)
10	HADDOCK FILLETS	25
8 fl oz (250 ml)	FISH STOCK	1 pt (570 ml)
2 oz (60 g)	POLYUNSATURATED MARGARINE	5 oz (140 g)
2 oz (60 g)	ONION, CHOPPED FINELY	5 oz (140 g)
3 oz (90 g)	WHOLEMEAL FLOUR	7 oz (200 g)
1 pt 5 fl oz (700 ml)	SKIMMED MILK	3 pt (1.75 l)
4 oz (115 g)	LOW-FAT CHEESE, GRATED	10 oz (285 g)

1 Steam or lightly boil spinach. Refresh under cold water and squeeze out surplus liquid.

2 Skin and bone fish. Fold fillets and cover with stock in a pan. Bring to boil and simmer gently for 5 minutes.

3 Make the sauce by melting margarine with onions and stirring in flour. Add milk slowly while stirring and simmer until cooked. Add three-quarters of the cheese and stir in.

4 Arrange spinach in bottom of heat-proof dish. Place fillets on top and cover with sauce. Sprinkle remaining cheese on top and heat under a grill until cheese melts and browns, serve hot.

NUTRIENT ANALYSIS PER PORTION			
	kcal	kJ	MINERALS & VITAMINS IN LARGE AMOUNTS
ENERGY (CALORIES)	238	995	
	GRAMS (g)	AS % TOTAL ENERGY	
TOTAL FAT	11.0	41.0	Potassium,
SATURATED FAT	2.6	9.9	calcium,
TOTAL CARBOHYDRATE	8.8	14.0	iron, zinc
ADDED SUGARS	–	–	Vitamins A,
PROTEIN	27.0	45.0	B group,
FIBRE	.8g		C, E,
SALT	1.15g		folic acid

FISH HARVEST BAKE

Rhonda Roberts
Auchenblae, Scotland

10 portions		25 portions
2	ONIONS	6
5 oz (140 g)	MUSHROOMS	12 oz (350 g)
4 oz (115 g)	FROZEN PEAS	10 oz (285 g)
2 pt (1.1 l)	SKIMMED MILK	5 pt (2.85 l)
1 oz (30 g)	SUNFLOWER OIL	3 oz (90 g)
5 oz (140 g)	WHOLEMEAL FLOUR	12 oz (350 g)
1 tbsp	PARSLEY, CHOPPED	2 tbsp
2 tsp	ENGLISH MUSTARD POWDER	1 tbsp
5 oz (140 g)	LOW-FAT CHEDDAR CHEESE	12 oz (350 g)
5	HADDOCK FILLETS	12
	Topping	
4 oz (115 g)	WHOLEMEAL FLOUR	12 oz (350 g)
2 oz (60 g)	POLYUNSATURATED MARGARINE	6 oz (170 g)
2½ oz (75 g)	TOASTED JUMBO OATS	6 oz (170 g)
2	SHREDDED WHEAT BISCUITS	6
1	TOMATO THINLY SLICED	2
¼	CUCUMBER, SLICED	½

1 Chop onions and slice mushrooms. Place in saucepan with frozen peas and just cover with milk. Bring to boil and simmer for 5 minutes or until onions are soft. Drain, reserving the liquid.

2 Heat oil in pan and stir in the flour. Remove from the heat and stir in the remaining milk and the reserved liquid. Bring to the boil, stirring continuously, and simmer until it thickens (3–5 minutes).

3 Add parsley, mustard and half the grated cheese and stir in the vegetables.

4 Place half the mixture in an oven-proof dish, make a layer of the fish fillets and pour over the remaining vegetable mixture.

5 Make the topping by rubbing the fat into the flour until it resembles breadcrumbs, stir in the oats, the crushed shredded wheat biscuits and remaining grated cheese. Sprinkle over the top of the dish. Bake in a moderate oven 375°F (190°C, gas mark 5) until golden brown on top.

Opposite: *Home-made Fish Cakes p. 125, Stuffed Courgettes p. 132, Mandarin Yoghurt Snow p. 198.*
Over Page: *Cannelloni stuffed with Lentils p. 165, Celery Apple and Sesame Salad p. 114, Apricot Mousse p. 198.*

6 Garnish with tomato and cucumber and serve hot with a baked potato and a side salad.

N U T R I E N T A N A L Y S I S P E R P O R T I O N			
	kcal	kJ	MINERALS &
ENERGY (CALORIES)	401	1676	VITAMINS IN
	GRAMS	AS % TOTAL	LARGE
	(g)	ENERGY	AMOUNTS
TOTAL FAT	14.0	31.0	Potassium,
SATURATED FAT	3.8	8.5	calcium,
TOTAL CARBOHYDRATE	38.0	36.0	iron, zinc
ADDED SUGARS	–	–	Vitamins
PROTEIN	33.0	33.0	B group,
FIBRE	6.6g		C, E
SALT	.98g		

HASTINGS FISH CRUMBLE

Miss H. B. Yeulett
Sussex

10 portions		25 portions
5	LEEKS, SLICED	12
5	LARGE CARROTS, SLICED	12
3	LARGE ONIONS, SLICED	7
2¹/2 oz (75 g)	POLYUNSATURATED MARGARINE	6¹/4 oz (180 g)
2¹/2 oz (75 g)	100% WHOLEMEAL FLOUR	6¹/4 oz (180 g)
12 fl oz (350 ml)	SKIMMED MILK	30 fl oz (850 ml)
12 fl oz (350 ml)	VEGETABLE STOCK	30 fl oz (850 ml)
2¹/2 tsp	MADE MUSTARD	7¹/2 tsp
1 lb 14 oz (735 g)	SWEETCORN, DRAINED	4 lb 11 oz (2.1 kg)
2¹/2 lb (1.13 kg)	COOKED WHITE FISH FILLET	6¹/4 lb (2.8 kg)
2¹/2 lb (1.13 kg)	TOMATOES, SLICED OR TINNED	6¹/4 lb (2.8 kg)
	Crumble	
5 oz (140 g)	ROLLED OATS	12¹/2 oz (365 g)
5 oz (140 g)	WHOLEMEAL BREADCRUMBS	12¹/2 oz (365 g)
5 oz (140 g)	LOW-FAT CHEESE, GRATED	12¹/2 oz (365 g)
	CAYENNE PEPPER (OPTIONAL)	

Previous Page: *Supreme of Maize-fed Chicken with Tomato Sauce p. 140, Nectarine and Raspberry Pancakes p. 188.*
Opposite: *Chicken and Tarragon Salad p. 116, Barley and Fruit Salad p. 119, Green Salad.*

1 Boil leeks, carrot and onion until tender.

2 Melt margarine, add flour and cook until mixture resembles breadcrumbs. Gradually stir in milk and stock. Cook until thickens.

3 Add mustard. Stir in vegetables and fish and transfer to oven-proof dish. Cover with sliced tomato.

4 Make crumble by combining oats, breadcrumbs, cayenne pepper and cheese. Sprinkle on top of cheese mixture and bake for 20–25 minutes at 400°F (200°C, gas mark 6) until crisp and golden.

5 Serve hot with jacket potatoes with a spoonful of low-fat yoghurt and a side salad.

NUTRIENT ANALYSIS PER PORTION			
	kcal	kJ	MINERALS &
ENERGY (CALORIES)	454	1898	VITAMINS IN
	GRAMS	AS % TOTAL	LARGE
	(g)	ENERGY	AMOUNTS
TOTAL FAT	12.0	24.0	Potassium,
SATURATED FAT	3.3	6.0	calcium,
TOTAL CARBOHYDRATE	49.0	41.0	zinc
ADDED SUGARS	5.4	4.5	Vitamins A,
PROTEIN	40.0	35.0	B group, C,
FIBRE	13.0g		folic acid
SALT	1.86g		

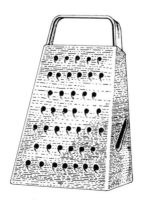

TINNED & SMOKED FISH

HADDOCK & LEEK POTATOES

Chris Gray
Southsea

10 portions		25 portions
10	BAKING POTATOES	25
1 lb (450 g)	SMOKED HADDOCK FILLET	2½ lb (1.1 kg)
1 lb (450 g)	LEEKS, TRIMMED AND CUT INTO RINGS	2½ lb (1.1 kg)
2½ oz (75 g)	POLYUNSATURATED MARGARINE	7¼ oz (200 g)
1 tbsp	GRAIN MUSTARD	2 tbsp
	PEPPER	
	NUTMEG	
½ pt (300 ml)	LOW-FAT NATURAL YOGHURT	1¼ pt (700 ml)
2½ oz (75 g)	EDAM, GRATED	7¼ oz (200 g)

1 Bake potatoes at 400°F (200°C, gas mark 6) for 1¼–1½ hours until tender.
Cool.

2 Poach haddock just covered with water for 10–15 minutes. Remove from
liquid and flake.

3 Boil leeks for 10 minutes. Drain.

4 Cut potatoes in half, scoop out middle into a bowl, retaining the shells for
filling.

5 Mash potato with margarine, mix in fish, leeks, mustard, pepper and nutmeg.
Add yoghurt. Mix well and spoon into potato shells.

6 Sprinkle with grated cheese, arrange on baking sheet and return to oven for
15 minutes.

NUTRIENT ANALYSIS PER PORTION			
	kcal	kJ	MINERALS &
ENERGY (CALORIES)	280	1170	VITAMINS IN
	GRAMS	AS % TOTAL	LARGE
	(g)	ENERGY	AMOUNTS
TOTAL FAT	8.8	28.0	Potassium
SATURATED FAT	2.4	7.8	Vitamins
TOTAL CARBOHYDRATE	38.0	51.0	B₆, C, E
ADDED SUGARS	–	–	
PROTEIN	14.0	21.0	
FIBRE	3.1g		
SALT	.56g		

STUFFED COURGETTES
Burley Manor Hotel & Restaurant
Burley

10 portions		25 portions
10	MEDIUM COURGETTES	25
2 lb 8 oz (1.1 kg)	SMOKED HADDOCK	6 lb 4 oz (2.80 kg)
1/2	LEMON	1
	BLACK PEPPER	
8	TOMATOES	18
8 oz (225 g)	FLAKED ALMONDS	1 lb 4 oz (550 g)
	PARSLEY FOR GARNISH	

1 Cut courgettes lengthwise, de-seed and blanch.

2 Poach haddock in lemon juice and a little water. Season with pepper.

3 Flake haddock and fill courgette halves. Lay sliced tomato on top, sprinkle with almonds and bake at 350°F (180°C, gas mark 4) for 7 minutes.

4 Serve two halves of courgette per portion sprinkled with chopped parsley.

NUTRIENT ANALYSIS PER PORTION			
	kcal	kJ	MINERALS &
ENERGY (CALORIES)	234	978	VITAMINS IN
	GRAMS	AS % TOTAL	LARGE
	(g)	ENERGY	AMOUNTS
TOTAL FAT	13.0	49.0	Potassium,
SATURATED FAT	1.1	4.4	zinc
TOTAL CARBOHYDRATE	4.5	7.3	Vitamins
ADDED SUGARS	–	–	B_2, B_6, B_{12},
PROTEIN	25.0	43.0	C, E
FIBRE	4.2g		
SALT	3.3g		

CRISPY PASTA CASSEROLE

Chris Gray
Southsea

10 portions		25 portions
11 oz (325 g)	WHOLEMEAL MACARONI	1 lb 12 oz (800 g)
1 pt (570 ml)	MILK	2½ pt (1.5 l)
3¼ oz (100 g)	FLOUR	8 oz (225 g)
8 oz (225 g)	LOW-FAT CHEDDAR CHEESE	1 lb 4 oz (565 g)
11 oz (325 g)	TUNA FISH	4 × 7 oz (800 g)
3 oz (90 g)	CANNED SWEETCORN, DRAINED	1 lb (450 g)
1 tbsp	PARSLEY, CHOPPED	4 tbsp
	PEPPER	
2 oz (60 g)	BREADCRUMBS	8 oz (225 g)
2 oz (60 g)	TOMATO FOR GARNISH	8 oz (225 g)

1 Cook macaroni until tender. Drain and keep warm.

2 Bring milk to near boiling. Mix flour with a little milk to a paste and stir in remainder of milk. Return to pan and simmer for 3 minutes. Add ¾ of the cheese and stir until melted.

3 Add sauce to pasta with the tuna fish, sweetcorn, parsley and seasoning. Mix well and tip into baking trays. Sprinkle rest of cheese and breadcrumbs on top.

4 Bake at 375°F (190°C, gas mark 5) for 30 minutes.

5 Garnish with tomato slices.

NUTRIENT ANALYSIS PER PORTION			
	kcal	kJ	MINERALS &
ENERGY (CALORIES)	321	1342	VITAMINS IN
	GRAMS	AS % TOTAL	LARGE
	(g)	ENERGY	AMOUNTS
TOTAL FAT	15.0	44.0	Potassium,
SATURATED FAT	6.1	17.0	calcium,
TOTAL CARBOHYDRATE	27.0	32.0	iron, zinc
ADDED SUGARS	–	–	Vitamins
PROTEIN	20.0	24.0	B_1, B_6, B_{12},
FIBRE	3.5g		nicotinic acid,
SALT	1.1g		E

TUNA GRATIN
Compass
London

10 portions		25 portions
6 oz (170 g)	ONIONS, SLICED	15 oz (430 g)
6 oz (170 g)	CARROTS	15 oz (430 g)
1	BAY LEAF	3
½ oz (15 g)	PEPPERCORNS, WHOLE	1¼ oz (38 g)
	MACE TO TASTE	
2 pt (1.1 l)	SKIMMED MILK	4 pt 10 fl oz (2.55 l)
2 lb 8 oz (1.1 kg)	BROCCOLI, SLICED	6 lb (2.75 kg)
1 lb 4 oz (565 g)	BUTTERBEANS, TINNED	3 lb (1.35 kg)
1 lb (450 g)	TUNA FISH IN BRINE, DRAINED	2 lb 12 oz (1.1 kg)
4 oz (115 g)	POLYUNSATURATED MARGARINE	8 oz (225 g)
5 oz (140 g)	WHOLEMEAL FLOUR	13 oz (380 g)
	PARMESAN CHEESE, GRATED, TO GARNISH	

1 Add onion, carrot, bay leaf, peppercorns and mace to milk and bring to boil gently. Remove from heat, cover and allow to cool.

2 Cook broccoli in a little water until just tender (5 minutes).

3 Heat butterbeans in a pan. Add the tuna, flaked, and broccoli.

4 Make a sauce by melting margarine in a pan, stirring in flour and slowly adding milk while stirring. Simmer 3–4 minutes and pour over tuna mixture. Sprinkle with parmesan and bake at 400°F (200°C, gas mark 6) for 20–30 minutes or until golden brown.

NUTRIENT ANALYSIS PER PORTION			
ENERGY (CALORIES)	kcal 300	kJ 1254	MINERALS & VITAMINS IN LARGE AMOUNTS
	GRAMS (g)	AS % TOTAL ENERGY	
TOTAL FAT	10.0	31.0	Potassium,
SATURATED FAT	2.1	6.3	calcium,
TOTAL CARBOHYDRATE	28.0	35.0	iron, zinc
ADDED SUGARS	–	–	Vitamins A,
PROTEIN	25.0	34.0	B group,
FIBRE	8.5g		C, D, E,
SALT	.98g		folic acid

TUNA PASTA SALAD

Angela Jacas
London

10 portions		25 portions
7 oz (200 g)	LOW FAT YOGHURT	1 lb 2 oz (520 g)
4 drops	TABASCO SAUCE	8–10 drops
	PINCH CHILLI	
1 tsp	PAPRIKA	2½ tsp
1 tbsp	SOY SAUCE	2½ tbsp
1	7½ oz (215 g) TIN, TUNA FISH	2½
1 lb 2 oz (520 g)	PASTA SHAPES, COOKED AL DENTE	2 lb 14 oz (1.25 kg)
5	TOMATOES, CHOPPED	12
½ bch	SPRING ONIONS, CHOPPED	1½ bch
1	GREEN PEPPER, DICED	3

1 Mix yoghurt, tabasco, chilli, paprika and soy sauce.
2 Flake tuna and mix gently with pasta, tomato, onions, green pepper.
3 Add yoghurt mixture and toss gently.

NUTRIENT ANALYSIS PER PORTION

	kcal	kJ	MINERALS & VITAMINS IN LARGE AMOUNTS
ENERGY (CALORIES)	281	1175	
	GRAMS (g)	AS % TOTAL ENERGY	
TOTAL FAT	6.3	20.0	Potassium
SATURATED FAT	1.3	4.0	Vitamins A,
TOTAL CARBOHYDRATE	45.0	61.0	nicotinic acid,
ADDED SUGARS	–	–	C, E, B$_{12}$
PROTEIN	14.0	20.0	
FIBRE	2.9g		
SALT	.35g		

SARDINE & PIZZA MUFFINS

Debbie Cooper
John Lewis Partnership

10 portions		25 portions
10	WHOLEMEAL MUFFINS, HALVED	25
1 lb (450 g)	CANNED SARDINES IN TOMATO SAUCE	2½ lb (1.1 kg)
1½ lb (675 g)	TOMATOES	3½ lb (1.5 kg)
1 lb (450 g)	LOW-FAT CHEDDAR CHEESE	2½ lb (1.1 kg)
1 tbsp	DRIED MIXED HERBS	2½ tbsp
	FEW STUFFED OLIVES FOR GARNISH	

1 Toast muffin halves lightly.

2 Lightly mash sardines and spread on muffins. Cover with layer of tomato slices, sprinkle with grated cheese and season with herbs.

3 Cook under medium grill until cheese begins to brown.

4 Serve two muffin halves per portion and garnish with slice of olive if desired.

A quick and easy recipe which can be adapted to other toppings:
- *Sweetcorn with tomato and cheese*
- *Tinned tuna and cheese*
- *Mushroom slices, tomato and cheese.*

NUTRIENT ANALYSIS PER PORTION			
	kcal	kJ	MINERALS & VITAMINS IN LARGE AMOUNTS
ENERGY (CALORIES)	267	1116	
	GRAMS (g)	AS % TOTAL ENERGY	
TOTAL FAT	12.0	42.0	Potassium,
SATURATED FAT	5.64	19.0	calcium, zinc
TOTAL CARBOHYDRATE	14.0	20.0	Vitamins B$_2$,
ADDED SUGARS	1.0	1.4	B$_{12}$, C, D
PROTEIN	25.0	38.0	
FIBRE	3.1g		
SALT	2.4g		

POULTRY

CHICKEN IN LEEK & CIDER SAUCE

Compass
London

10 portions		25 portions
10	CHICKEN PORTIONS	25
4 oz (115 g)	SOYA OIL	7 oz (200 g)
2 lb 8 oz (1.1 kg)	LEEKS, SLICED	6 lb 4 oz (2.8 kg)
4 oz (115 g)	WHOLEMEAL FLOUR	8 oz (225 g)
1 pt 10 fl oz (850 ml)	SKIMMED MILK	3 pt 15 fl oz (2.2 l)
1 pt 10 fl oz (850 ml)	DRY CIDER	3 pt 15 fl oz (2.2 l)
	ROSEMARY AND THYME TO TASTE	
2	BAY LEAVES	9

1 Fry chicken 2–3 minutes each side in oil. Remove and keep warm.

2 Fry leeks for several minutes until soft, stir in flour followed by milk while stirring. Add cider, bring to boil and simmer for 3 minutes. Add herbs.

3 Add chicken to sauce and continue simmering for 30 minutes until chicken is tender.

NUTRIENT ANALYSIS PER PORTION			
	kcal	kJ	MINERALS & VITAMINS IN LARGE AMOUNTS
ENERGY (CALORIES)	370	1547	
	GRAMS (g)	AS % TOTAL ENERGY	
TOTAL FAT	13.0	32.0	Potassium,
SATURATED FAT	2.8	6.7	calcium,
TOTAL CARBOHYDRATE	21.0	21.0	iron, zinc
ADDED SUGARS	–	–	Vitamins B_1,
PROTEIN	37.0	40.0	B_2, B_6, C, E
FIBRE	4.5g		
SALT	.42g		

POULET SAUTÉ STANLEY

Leith's Good Food
London

10 portions		25 portions
2 × 3 lb (1.35 kg)	CHICKENS	5 × 3 lb (1.35 kg)
	PEPPER	
6 tsp	GRAPESEED OIL	15 tsp
4	MEDIUM ONIONS, SLICED	10
4	GARLIC CLOVES	8
2 tbsp	CURRY POWDER	5 tbsp
7 fl oz (200 ml)	WHITE WINE	21 fl oz (600 ml)
12 oz (350 g)	BUTTON MUSHROOMS	1 lb 14 oz (850 g)
4 oz (115 g)	CREAM	10 oz (285 g)
4 oz (115 g)	GREEK YOGHURT	10 oz (285 g)

1 Cut each chicken into 10 portions, generously pepper and seal in a casserole with the oil. Remove chicken and the oil from the top of any juices.

2 Sweat onion and garlic in casserole. Add curry powder for another minute. Add white wine and reduce for 3 minutes, then add stock.

3 Add chicken and mushrooms then cook for 30 minutes at 375°F (190°C, gas mark 5).

4 Remove chicken and mushrooms. Keep warm.

5 Strain juices in chinois sieve and skim fat. Add cream to juices and reduce 5 minutes on low heat while stirring. Liquidise reduced sauce with half onion from the sieve. Mix yoghurt with little of the hot sauce, add remaining onions from sieve and pour back into rest of hot sauce.

6 Serve hot with chicken arranged on serving dish anointed with the hot sauce.

NUTRIENT ANALYSIS PER PORTION			
ENERGY (CALORIES)	kcal 227	kJ 949	MINERALS & VITAMINS IN LARGE AMOUNTS
	GRAMS (g)	AS % TOTAL ENERGY	
TOTAL FAT	12.0	47.0	Potassium,
SATURATED FAT	4.3	17.0	iron, zinc
TOTAL CARBOHYDRATE	4.4	7.3	Vitamins B_2,
ADDED SUGARS	–	–	nicotinic acid,
PROTEIN	23.0	41.0	C
FIBRE	1.7g		
SALT	.25g		

BAKED CHICKEN WITH COURGETTE STUFFING

Leith's Good Food
London

10 portions		25 portions
2 lb (900 g)	COURGETTES	5 lb (2.3 kg)
2	ONIONS	5
2	GARLIC CLOVES	5
1 tbsp	SOYA OIL	2½ tbsp
8 oz (225 g)	RICOTTA CHEESE	1 lb 8 oz (675 g)
2	BOUQUET GARNI	4
2 tsp	FINES HERBES, CHOPPED	5 tsp
½ tsp	HERBES DE PROVENCE, DRIED	1 tsp
2 oz (60 g)	PARMESAN, GRATED	5 oz (140 g)
2	EGG WHITES, BEATEN	5
4 oz (115 g)	BREADCRUMBS	10 oz (285 g)
2 × 3½ lb (1.5 kg)	CHICKENS	4 × 4 lb (1.8 kg)

1 Make a stuffing by grating courgettes. Sweat onions and garlic in oil then add courgettes for two minutes. Remove and spread on large serving dish to cool.

2 Soften ricotta in a bowl and add cooled vegetables, herbs, parmesan and finally egg whites and breadcrumbs.

3 Bone chickens and lay flat, skin side up. Separate skin from flesh with fingers and fill cavity with stuffing. Roast chicken in a tin lined with foil for 40–50 minutes at 350°F (180°C, gas mark 4) or until golden brown.

4 Remove chicken letting fat drain back into tin and serve with a choice of vegetables and salad leaves.

NUTRIENT ANALYSIS PER PORTION			
	kcal	kJ	MINERALS &
ENERGY (CALORIES)	271	1133	VITAMINS IN
	GRAMS	AS % TOTAL	LARGE
	(g)	ENERGY	AMOUNTS
TOTAL FAT	11.0	37.0	Potassium,
SATURATED FAT	4.2	14.0	calcium, zinc
TOTAL CARBOHYDRATE	11.0	15.0	Vitamins B_2,
ADDED SUGARS	–	–	B_6, B_{12},
PROTEIN	32.0	48.0	nicotinic acid,
FIBRE	1.0g		C
SALT	.66g		

SUPREME OF MAIZE-FED CHICKEN WITH TOMATO SAUCE

Chester Boyd Ltd
London

10 portions		25 portions
1	LARGE ONION, CHOPPED	2
	OIL	
3 lb (1.35 kg)	RIPE TOMATOES	7 lb (3.2 kg)
2 oz (60 g)	PARSLEY, CHOPPED	5 oz (140 g)
10	BREASTS OF CHICKEN (MAIZE-FED PREFERRED)	25
1 pt (570 ml)	CHICKEN STOCK	2 pt (1.1 l)
½ bottle	DRY WHITE WINE OR VERMOUTH	1 bottle
	PEPPERCORNS, BAY LEAVES	
3 lb (1.35 kg)	NEW POTATOES	7 lb (3.2 kg)
3 lb (1.35 kg)	MIXED VEGETABLES, CUT INTO JULIENNE STRIPS – INCLUDING CARROTS, TURNIPS, CELERIAC, PEPPERS, LEEKS, ONIONS, CELERY, MANGE-TOUTS	7 lb (3.2 kg)
	PARSLEY FOR GARNISH	

1 Make a sauce with chopped onion sweated in a little oil followed by tomatoes, roughly chopped, and parsley. Reduce to a thick sauce.

2 Poach breasts in the wine and stock with peppercorns and bay leaves.

3 Boil new potatoes.

4 Stir-fry vegetables ensuring they remain crisp.

5 Serve by laying a bed of vegetables with a breast on top; place potatoes on one side and sauce on other. Garnish with herbs.

NUTRIENT ANALYSIS PER PORTION			
	kcal	kJ	MINERALS & VITAMINS IN LARGE AMOUNTS
ENERGY (CALORIES)	242	1012	
	GRAMS (g)	AS % TOTAL ENERGY	
TOTAL FAT	3.7	14.0	Potassium,
SATURATED FAT	1.3	4.7	iron, zinc
TOTAL CARBOHYDRATE	17.0	27.0	Vitamins A,
ADDED SUGARS	1.2	1.9	B_1, B_6, C, E,
PROTEIN	27.0	45.0	nicotinic acid,
FIBRE	5g		folic acid
SALT	.45g		

CHICKEN BREASTS WITH CHILLI & GINGER

Leith's Good Food
London

10 portions		25 portions
10	SAVOY CABBAGE LEAVES	25
3	SMALL GREEN CHILLI	8
½ in (1.25 cm)	GINGER ROOT, PEELED AND CHOPPED	2¼ in (5.75 cm)
10	CHICKEN BREASTS	25
	SESAME OIL	

1 Blanch cabbage leaves and refresh under cold water. Drain.
2 Chop chillis and mix with ginger.
3 Skin chicken breasts. Divide chilli and ginger among breasts and roll each one in a cabbage leaf. Steam over boiling water for 15–20 minutes and serve sprinkled with a few drops of sesame oil.

NUTRIENT ANALYSIS PER PORTION			
	kcal	kJ	MINERALS & VITAMINS IN LARGE AMOUNTS
ENERGY (CALORIES)	182	761	
	GRAMS (g)	AS % TOTAL ENERGY	
TOTAL FAT	5.7	28.0	Potassium
SATURATED FAT	1.7	8.4	Vitamins B$_6$,
TOTAL CARBOHYDRATE	.5	1.0	nicotinic acid
ADDED SUGARS	–	–	
PROTEIN	32.0	71.0	
FIBRE	.6g		
SALT	.27g		

CHICKEN MIMOSA

Moorland Links Hotel
Yelverton

10 portions		25 portions
3	3½ LB (1.5 KG) FRESH CHICKENS	8
3	CELERY STALKS	8
1	LARGE SPANISH ONION	3
1	LEEK, WHITE STEM ONLY	3
1	BOUQUET GARNI	2

3 fl oz (75 ml)	*SOYA OIL*	*7½ fl oz (215 ml)*
1	*LEMON*	*2*
	WHITE PEPPER	
3 oz (90 g)	*PLAIN FLOUR*	*7½ oz (215 g)*
15 fl oz (450 ml)	*LOW-FAT NATURAL YOGHURT*	*37½ fl oz (1 l)*
4 fl oz (100 ml)	*WATER*	*10 fl oz (300 ml)*
3 tsp	*CORNFLOUR*	*7½ tsp*
	GROUND NUTMEG	
3 tbsp	*PARSLEY, CHOPPED*	*7½ tbsp*
4 oz (115 g)	*SULTANAS*	*10 oz (285 g)*
4	*LARGE ORANGES, IN SEGMENTS*	*10*
2	*BANANAS*	*5*
10 oz (285 g)	*BLACK GRAPES, HALVED AND DESEEDED*	*25 oz (700 g)*
2	*LETTUCE HEARTS*	*5*

1 Skin chicken, remove all visible fat and cut into pieces.

2 Make a 1½ pt (850 ml) or 3¾ pt (2.2 l) stock with the wings, carcase, celery, onion, leek and bouquet garni.

3 Grease an ovenproof dish with a little oil and line with chicken pieces. Sprinkle with lemon and pepper. Cover and poach gently for 30 minutes in oven at 325°F (160°C, gas mark 3).

4 Make a roux with the remaining oil and the flour. Add the chicken stock slowly while stirring and simmer gently until cooked. Strain sauce.

5 Blend ⅔ of yoghurt with water, cornflour, a pinch of nutmeg and a third of parsley. Add to sauce. Reheat but do not boil.

6 Arrange chicken on serving plate, sprinkle with sultanas and coat with sauce. Surround with fruit mixed with remaining yoghurt and garnish with quartered lettuce hearts and parsley.

NUTRIENT ANALYSIS PER PORTION			
	kcal	kJ	MINERALS &
ENERGY (CALORIES)	354	1480	VITAMINS IN
	GRAMS	AS % TOTAL	LARGE
	(g)	ENERGY	AMOUNTS
TOTAL FAT	13.0	33.0	Potassium,
SATURATED FAT	3.3	8.4	calcium,
TOTAL CARBOHYDRATE	34.0	36.0	iron, zinc
ADDED SUGARS	–	–	Vitamins A,
PROTEIN	28.0	32.0	B_2, B_6,
FIBRE	4.5g		nicotinic acid,
SALT	.54g		C

TANDOORI CHICKEN

Judith Liddel
Aberdeen

10 portions		25 portions
2 tbsp	SUNFLOWER OIL	5 tbsp
2 tsp	LEMON JUICE	2 tbsp
10 fl oz (300 ml)	NATURAL LOW-FAT YOGHURT	1.25 pt (700 ml)
1½ oz (45 g)	TOMATO PURÉE	3.5 oz (105 g)
10	GARLIC CLOVES	25
1 tsp	CURRY POWDER	1 tbsp
2 tbsp	TANDOORI POWDER	5 tbsp
1 tsp	TURMERIC	1 tbsp
10	CHICKEN PORTIONS	25
2 lb 3 oz (990 g)	BROWN RICE	5 lb 8 oz (2.5 kg)

1 Mix oil and lemon juice. Add yoghurt, tomato, garlic, curry powder, tandoori powder, turmeric and mix well.

2 Cut chicken portions across, coat in sauce and marinate for 12 hours in fridge.

3 Line a baking tin with chicken pieces and bake at 350°F (180°C, gas mark 4) for 45 minutes. Brown under a grill.

4 Serve on a bed of boiled brown rice.

NUTRIENT ANALYSIS PER PORTION			
	kcal	kJ	MINERALS &
ENERGY (CALORIES)	513	2144	VITAMINS IN
	GRAMS	AS % TOTAL	LARGE
	(g)	ENERGY	AMOUNTS
TOTAL FAT	10.0	18.0	Potassium,
SATURATED FAT	2.5	4.4	iron, zinc
TOTAL CARBOHYDRATE	85.0	62.0	Vitamins
ADDED SUGARS	–	–	B group,
PROTEIN	26.0	20.0	E
FIBRE	4.5g		
SALT	.25g		

CHICKEN & PINEAPPLE CHOP SUEY

Aberdeen Royal Infirmary, Aberdeen

10 portions		25 portions
1.5 lb (675 g)	COOKED CHICKEN	3 lb 12 oz (1.6 kg)
8 oz (225 g)	ONIONS, SLICED	1 lb 4 oz (550 g)
	SOYA OIL	
8 oz (225 g)	GREEN PEPPERS, CHOPPED	1 lb 4 oz (550 g)
1 oz (30 g)	CORNFLOUR	2½ oz (60 g)
10½ oz (300 g)	CANNED PINEAPPLE PIECES	1 lb 12½ oz (800 g)
1 lb (450 g)	MUSHROOMS	2 lb 8 oz (1.1 kg)
	SOYA SAUCE TO TASTE	
1 oz (30 ml)	SHERRY	2½ oz (60 ml)
8 pt (4.5 l)	CHICKEN STOCK	20 pt (11.25 l)
	PEPPER TO TASTE	
8 oz (225 g)	BEANSPROUTS	1 lb 4 oz (550 g)

1 Cut chicken into small pieces.

2 Sweat onion for few minutes and add peppers for another 2–3 minutes.

3 Mix cornflour with pineapple juice. Add with chicken and mushrooms to pan. Boil and simmer.

4 Add soya sauce, sherry, stock and seasoning. Simmer 5 minutes.

5 Add beansprouts and pineapple. Simmer for 1 minute. Serve on a bed of rice.

NUTRIENT ANALYSIS PER PORTION			
	kcal	kJ	MINERALS & VITAMINS IN LARGE AMOUNTS
ENERGY (CALORIES)	170	711	
	GRAMS (g)	AS % TOTAL ENERGY	
TOTAL FAT	5.2	28.0	Potassium,
SATURATED FAT	1.6	8.6	iron
TOTAL CARBOHYDRATE	12.0	27.0	Vitamins B_2,
ADDED SUGARS	2.9	6.3	B_6, B_{12},
PROTEIN	19.0	44.0	nicotinic acid,
FIBRE	2.1g		C
SALT	.7g		

SMOKED CHICKEN SALAD

Burley Manor Hotel & Restaurant
Burley

10 portions		25 portions
2 lb (900 g)	SMOKED CHICKEN	5 lb 8 oz (2.5 kg)
2 lb (900 g)	BEAN SPROUTS	5 lb (2.3 kg)
8 oz (225 g)	CASHEW NUTS	1 lb 4 oz (550 g)
2	LEMONS	5
	PEPPER	
1½	ICEBERG LETTUCE	4

1 Cut chicken into julienne strips and add to bean sprouts and nuts.
2 Squeeze lemon juice over, season with pepper and mix. Lay on a bed of shredded lettuce.

NUTRIENT ANALYSIS PER PORTION			
	kcal	kJ	MINERALS & VITAMINS IN LARGE AMOUNTS
ENERGY (CALORIES)	320	1334	
	GRAMS (g)	AS % TOTAL ENERGY	
TOTAL FAT	16.0	46.0	Potassium,
SATURATED FAT	2.9	8.1	iron, zinc
TOTAL CARBOHYDRATE	12.0	14.0	Vitamins A,
ADDED SUGARS	–	–	B group,
PROTEIN	32.0	40.0	C, E,
FIBRE	4.1g		folic acid
SALT	.25g		

HOME-MADE CHINESE PANCAKE ROLLS

Debbie Cooper
John Lewis Partnership

10 portions		25 portions
4 oz (115 g)	WHOLEMEAL FLOUR	10 oz (285 g)
4 oz (115 g)	WHITE FLOUR	10 oz (285 g)
2	EGGS	5
1 pt (570 ml)	SEMI-SKILLED MILK	2½ pt (1.5 l)

5 oz (140 g)	*BUTTON MUSHROOMS*	*12 oz (350 g)*
4 oz (115 g)	*RED PEPPER*	*10 oz (285 g)*
1 bunch	*SPRING ONIONS*	*2½ bunches*
3 fl oz (75 ml)	*SUNFLOWER OIL*	*6 fl oz (180 ml)*
4 oz (115 g)	*GRATED CARROT*	*10 oz (285 g)*
12 oz (350 g)	*DICED, COOKED CHICKEN MEAT*	*1¾ lb (800 g)*
1 tsp	*DRIED GINGER*	*2½ tsp*
4 fl oz (100 ml)	*SOY SAUCE*	*8 fl oz (250 ml)*
8 oz (225 g)	*BEAN SPROUTS*	*1¼ lb (565 g)*
3 fl oz (75 ml)	*LEMON JUICE*	*6 fl oz (180 ml)*

1 Put flours in mixing bowl. Make a well and add the eggs plus half the milk. Mix to a smooth batter, then beat in remaining milk. Let stand 20 minutes.

2 Make 20 (or 50) pancakes from the batter. Keep hot.

3 Slice mushrooms and red pepper. Trim and chop onions.

4 Heat a small amount of oil in a heavy pan and fry together the carrot, red pepper, chicken, mushrooms, the ginger and most of the onions. Stir-fry for 2 minutes. Add half the soy sauce and the bean sprouts and stir-fry for another minute.

5 Fill pancakes with mixture and roll them up.

6 Mix lemon juice, soy sauce and reserved onions to make a sauce. Serve two pancakes per portion and anoint with some sauce.

The filling will deteriorate if kept warm too long, so batch-cook pancakes and filling as required.

NUTRIENT ANALYSIS PER PORTION			
	kcal	kJ	MINERALS &
ENERGY (CALORIES)	308	1287	VITAMINS IN
	GRAMS	AS % TOTAL	LARGE
	(g)	ENERGY	AMOUNTS
TOTAL FAT	17.0	49.0	Potassium,
SATURATED FAT	4.0	12.0	calcium,
TOTAL CARBOHYDRATE	24.0	29.0	iron, zinc
ADDED SUGARS	–	–	Vitamins
PROTEIN	17.0	23.0	A, B_2,
FIBRE	2.8g		nicotinic acid,
SALT	.25g		C, E

CHOW MEIN (CHICKEN, PORK OR BEEF)

Sick Children's Hospital
Aberdeen

10 portions		25 portions
1.2 lb (540 g)	CHICKEN BREAST, PORK OR BEEF, CUT IN STRIPS OR SMALL PIECES	3 lb (1.35 kg)
	SOYA OIL	
10 oz (285 g)	ONIONS, SLICED	1 lb 9 oz (705 g)
1/4	CABBAGE, SLICED AND CHOPPED	2/3
10 oz (285 g)	MUSHROOMS, SLICED	1 lb 9 oz (705 g)
3 oz (90 g)	PEPPERS, CHOPPED	7 1/2 oz (210 g)
13 oz (360 g)	BEANSPROUTS	2 lb (900 g)
5 oz (140 g)	NOODLES	12 1/2 oz (365 g)
2 fl oz (50 ml)	SHERRY	5 fl oz (150 ml)
	SOYA SAUCE TO TASTE	

1 Stir-fry meat in oil. Remove meat and stir-fry onions, cabbage, mushrooms, peppers and beansprouts, making sure peppers stay crisp.

2 Boil noodles. Drain and add to vegetables in wok. Return meat, add bean sprouts and stir for 3 minutes on heat. Add sherry and soya sauce. Serve hot.

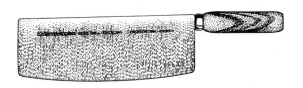

NUTRIENT ANALYSIS PER PORTION			
	kcal	kJ	MINERALS & VITAMINS IN LARGE AMOUNTS
ENERGY (CALORIES)	153	640	
	GRAMS (g)	AS % TOTAL ENERGY	
TOTAL FAT	3.3	20.0	Potassium
SATURATED FAT	.8	4.8	Vitamin C,
TOTAL CARBOHYDRATE	14.0	35.0	nicotinic acid
ADDED SUGARS	.1	.1	
PROTEIN	16.0	42.0	
FIBRE	2.9g		
SALT	.13g		

TOMATO, SMOKED CHICKEN & FROMAGE BLANC PIZZA

Leith's Good Food
London

10 portions		25 portions
1 tsp	FRESH YEAST	2½ tsp
10 fl oz (300 ml)	WATER	1 pt 10 fl oz (850 ml)
1 lb (450 g)	FLOUR	2 lb 8 oz (1.1 kg)
2 tbsp	SOYA OIL	5 tbsp
4 tbsp	TOMATO PURÉE	10 tbsp
1 tsp	OREGANO, DRIED	2½ tsp
½ tsp	BASIL, FRIED	1 tsp
1 lb 12 oz (800 g)	CANNED TOMATOES	4 lb 8 oz (1.8 kg)
8 oz (225 g)	SMOKED CHICKEN, CUT IN PIECES	1 lb 8 oz (675 g)
8 oz (225 g)	FROMAGE BLANC	1 lb 8 oz (675 g)

1 Make a dough by dissolving yeast in water, adding to flour plus the oil, mixing and kneading until elastic. Let prove.

2 Knead again and line a deep sandwich tin, pulling dough up sides.

3 Mix purée and herbs. Spread on dough.

4 Cut tomatoes in half, drain *very* well and place on absorbent paper. Arrange on pizza base. Place smoked chicken pieces on top and bake at 475°F (240°C, gas mark 9) for 15 minutes.

5 Spoon blobs of fromage blanc on top and continue baking for further 5 minutes.

NUTRIENT ANALYSIS PER PORTION			
ENERGY (CALORIES)	kcal 226	kJ 945	MINERALS & VITAMINS IN LARGE AMOUNTS
	GRAMS (g)	AS % TOTAL ENERGY	
TOTAL FAT	3.4	14.0	Potassium
SATURATED FAT	.7	2.7	Vitamin C,
TOTAL CARBOHYDRATE	38.0	63.0	nicotinic acid
ADDED SUGARS	—	—	
PROTEIN	13.0	24.0	
FIBRE	2.2g		
SALT	.31g		

TURKEY, SWEETCORN & MUSHROOM PIE

Stuart Cabeldu Catering Ltd
London

10 portions		25 portions
	White sauce	
3 oz (90 g)	POLYUNSATURATED MARGARINE	7 oz (200 g)
3 oz (90 g)	PLAIN FLOUR	7 oz (200 g)
1 pt 4 fl oz (670 ml)	SKIMMED MILK	3½ pt (2 l)
	Pastry	
13 oz (375 g)	SOLID VEGETABLE SHORTENING	2 lb (900 g)
13 oz (375 g)	WHOLEMEAL FLOUR	2 lb (900 g)
13 oz (375 g)	PLAIN FLOUR	2 lb (900 g)
5 fl oz (150 ml)	WATER	13 fl oz (380 ml)
2 lb 8 oz (1.13 kg)	TURKEY MEAT, COOKED AND DICED	7 lb (3.2 kg)
13 oz (375 g)	SWEETCORN	2 lb (900 g)
13 oz (375 g)	BUTTON MUSHROOMS	2 lb (900 g)

1 Make a white sauce by making a roux and adding milk slowly while stirring. Continue stirring until cooked.

2 Make the pastry by rubbing fat into the mixed flours until it resembles fine breadcrumbs. Add water and mix.

3 Mix turkey, sweetcorn and whole mushrooms with white sauce. Place in a pie dish and cover with rolled pastry. Bake at 400°F (200°C, gas mark 6) for 15 minutes or until golden.

NUTRIENT ANALYSIS PER PORTION			
	kcal	kJ	MINERALS &
ENERGY (CALORIES)	897	3749	VITAMINS IN
	GRAMS (g)	AS % TOTAL ENERGY	LARGE AMOUNTS
TOTAL FAT	49.0	50.0	Potassium,
SATURATED FAT	10.0	10.0	calcium,
TOTAL CARBOHYDRATE	71.0	30.0	iron, zinc
ADDED SUGARS	2.8	1.2	Vitamins
PROTEIN	46.0	21.0	B group, E
FIBRE	8.3g		
SALT	7.4g		

MEAT

POACHED MIGNOTTES OF BEEF WITH BABY LEEKS, CARROTS & LENTILS

John McManus
London

10 portions		25 portions
1 lb 14 oz (860 g)	GREEN LENTILS (SOAKED OVERNIGHT)	4 lb 11 oz (2.1 kg)
10 pt (5.75 l)	VEAL STOCK	18 pt (10.75 l)
2	ONIONS	4
4	CARROTS	8
2	CLOVES GARLIC	4
1	SPRIG THYME	2
3 lb 12 oz (1.7 kg)	BEEF FILLET	9 lb 4 oz (4.25 kg)
12 oz (350 g)	BABY LEEKS	1 lb 14 oz (610 g)
1 lb (450 g)	BABY CARROTS	2 lb 8 oz (1.1 kg)
12 oz (350 g)	BUTTON ONIONS	1 lb 14 oz (610 g)

1 Wash soaked lentils and cover with cold veal stock. Add onion, carrot, garlic and thyme. Cover and boil until lentils are tender.

2 Cut beef into 3 oz (90 g) pieces. Cut carrots and leeks into 2½ in (6 cm) lengths and boil separately until tender. Peel button onions and cook in veal stock until tender. Keep hot.

3 Heat remainder of the stock and poach the beef in it to desired degree of cooking (rare, medium, etc.).

4 Serve by making a bed of lentils on a plate, placing beef on top and arranging the vegetables around the edge. Lightly coat with hot veal stock.

NUTRIENT ANALYSIS PER PORTION			
ENERGY (CALORIES)	kcal 526	kJ 2199	MINERALS & VITAMINS IN LARGE AMOUNTS
	GRAMS (g)	AS % TOTAL ENERGY	
TOTAL FAT	9.0	15.0	Potassium,
SATURATED FAT	3.3	5.7	calcium,
TOTAL CARBOHYDRATE	56.0	40.0	iron, zinc
ADDED SUGARS	–	–	Vitamins A,
PROTEIN	59.0	49.0	B group,
FIBRE	14.0g		C, E,
SALT	1.9g		nicotinic acid, folic acid

VEAL SCALLOPS WITH CUCUMBER & PEACHES

Leith's Good Food
London

10 portions		25 portions
2	CUCUMBER	5
4	PEACHES	10
10 fl oz (300 ml)	MEAT STOCK	1 pt 5 fl oz (700 ml)
2 lb 8 oz (1.1 kg)	VEAL SCALLOPS	6 lb 4 oz (2.8 kg)
	SUNFLOWER OIL	
	BLACK PEPPER	
	FRESH MINT, FOR GARNISH	

1 Peel cucumber, cut in halves lengthwise and scoop out seeds. Cut in chunks. Blanch peaches and remove skins and stones, then cut into eight segments.

2 Cook cucumber in stock for four minutes, add peaches and simmer for two minutes. Remove with slotted spoon and drain.

3 Trim fat from veal. Brush with sunflower oil, sprinkle with black pepper and grill for two minutes a side.

4 Arrange scallops on serving dish, garnish with cucumber and peaches with a topping of chopped fresh mint.

NUTRIENT ANALYSIS PER PORTION			
	kcal	kJ	MINERALS & VITAMINS IN
ENERGY (CALORIES)	177	740	
	GRAMS (g)	AS % TOTAL ENERGY	LARGE AMOUNTS
TOTAL FAT	5.1	26.0	Potassium,
SATURATED FAT	1.5	7.6	iron, zinc
TOTAL CARBOHYDRATE	8.8	19.0	Vitamins B$_2$,
ADDED SUGARS	–	–	B$_6$, B$_{12}$,
PROTEIN	24.0	55.0	nicotinic acid,
FIBRE	1.4g		C
SALT	.47g		

CARIBBEAN PIE

Angela Jacas
London

10 portions		25 portions
2 lb (900 g)	MINCED LEAN BEEF OR PORK	5 lb (2.3 kg)
2	LARGE ONIONS, SLICED	4
1 tsp	THYME	2½
1 dsp	CHOPPED PARSLEY	2½ dsp
2	CLOVES GARLIC, CRUSHED	5
2 pt (1.1 l)	STOCK	5 pt (2.85 l)
2 tsp	WORCESTERSHIRE SAUCE	5 tsp
2 lb (900 g)	COOKED BROWN RICE	5 lb (2.3 kg)
1 oz (30 g)	GOLDEN BREADCRUMBS	2½ oz (75 g)
1 tsp	PAPRIKA	2½ tsp

1 Heat mince in pan on low heat, add onion, thyme, parsley and garlic.

2 Add enough stock to cover meat, add the Worcestershire sauce and simmer covered for 15 minutes.

3 Place half the rice in a greased ovenproof dish, cover with meat mixture, add remainder of stock and the remainder of the rice.

4 Sprinkle with breadcrumbs and the paprika. Bake in medium oven at 350°F (180°C, gas mark 4) for 40 minutes.

5 Serve hot with vegetables.

NUTRIENT ANALYSIS PER PORTION			
	kcal	kJ	MINERALS & VITAMINS IN LARGE AMOUNTS
ENERGY (CALORIES)	280	1170	
	GRAMS (g)	AS % TOTAL ENERGY	
TOTAL FAT	7.2	23.0	Potassium,
SATURATED FAT	2.6	8.4	iron, zinc
TOTAL CARBOHYDRATE	31.0	42.0	Vitamins B_1,
ADDED SUGARS	–	–	B_6, B_{12},
PROTEIN	25.0	35.0	nicotinic acid,
FIBRE	3.0g		C
SALT	.17g		

VENISON WITH PLUMS

Leith's Good Food
London

10 portions		25 portions
3 lb 8 oz (1.5 kg)	VENISON	9 lb (4 kg)
2 tbsp	SOYA OIL	5 tbsp
4	ONIONS, SLICED	10
4 tbsp	FLOUR	10 tbsp
2 pt (1.1 l)	STOCK	5 pt (2.85 l)
2 tbsp	VINEGAR	5 tbsp
18	PLUMS, STONED AND QUARTERED	45

1 Cut venison into 2 in (5 cm) cubes, trimming away any fat or membrane.

2 Heat oil in pan, add meat and brown well. Remove to casserole and replace with onions for light browning.

3 Add flour to pan. Heat for 30 seconds, add stock and boil, stirring. Simmer for 2 minutes then pour over venison. Add vinegar and plums to casserole.

4 Cover and bake for 1½–2 hours at 325°F (160°C, gas mark 3) or until very tender.

Like all casseroles, this dish is particularly good if made a day in advance and reheated.

NUTRIENT ANALYSIS PER PORTION			
	kcal	kJ	MINERALS &
ENERGY (CALORIES)	260	1087	VITAMINS IN
	GRAMS (g)	AS % TOTAL ENERGY	LARGE AMOUNTS
TOTAL FAT	9.7	34.0	Potassium,
SATURATED FAT	.6	2.0	iron
TOTAL CARBOHYDRATE	12.0	17.0	Vitamin C
ADDED SUGARS	–	–	
PROTEIN	32.0	49.0	
FIBRE	2.3g		
SALT	.34g		

COUNTRY LIVER

Debbie Cooper
John Lewis Partnership

10 portions		25 portions
8 oz (225 g)	ONIONS	1¼ lb (565 g)
2 dsp	SUNFLOWER OIL	4 dsp
2 oz (60 g)	FRESH SAGE	5 oz (140 g)
2½ lb (1.1 kg)	LAMB'S LIVER	6¼ lb (2.8 kg)
2 oz (60 g)	WHOLEMEAL FLOUR	5 oz (140 g)
¾ pt (450 ml)	APPLE JUICE	1¾ pt (1 l)
½ tsp	GROUND CLOVES	1 tsp
12 oz (350 g)	COX'S APPLES	1¾ lb (800 g)
	BLACK PEPPER	

1 Slice onion and heat in a pan with the oil for 2 minutes. Add the sage and cook for 1 minute more.

2 Cut liver into strips and dust with flour, add to the onions and cook briskly for 5 minutes, turning strips once. Stir in apple juice, ground cloves and season with pepper. Bring to boil while stirring.

3 Peel, core and chop apples then add them and simmer for 2 minutes. Serve hot.

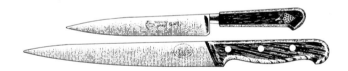

NUTRIENT ANALYSIS PER PORTION			
	kcal	kJ	MINERALS &
ENERGY (CALORIES)	271	1133	VITAMINS IN
	GRAMS	AS % TOTAL	LARGE
	(g)	ENERGY	AMOUNTS
TOTAL FAT	13.0	45.0	Potassium,
SATURATED FAT	3.6	12.0	iron, copper,
TOTAL CARBOHYDRATE	15.0	21.0	zinc
ADDED SUGARS	–	–	Vitamins A,
PROTEIN	23.0	34.0	B group,
FIBRE	1.1g		C, E,
SALT	.22g		folic acid

VEGETARIAN MAIN COURSES

BEAN STEW & WHOLEMEAL DUMPLINGS (V,VG)

Rivers L W, Oxford

10 portions		25 portions
1 lb (450 g)	ONIONS, CHOPPED ROUGHLY	2 lb 8 oz (1.1 kg)
2 lb 8 oz (1.1 kg)	CARROTS, DICED	3 lb 12 oz (1.55 kg)
6 oz (170 g)	CELERY, CHOPPED	15 oz (430 g)
1 lb (450 g)	TURNIPS, DICED	2 lb 8 oz (1.1 kg)
2 lb (900 g)	SWEDE, DICED	5 lb (2.3 kg)
2 tbsp	SUNFLOWER OIL	5 tbsp
1 lb 4 oz (565 g)	CANNED KIDNEY BEANS	3 lb 2 oz (1.4 kg)
1 lb 4 oz (565 g)	CANNED BUTTER BEANS	3 lb 2 oz (1.4 kg)
8 oz (225 g)	CANNED HARICOT BEANS	1 lb 4 oz (565 g)
5 pt (2.83 l)	VEGETABLE STOCK	12½ pt (7.1 l)
1 dsp	OREGANO, DRIED	2½ dsp
1 dsp	SAGE	2½ dsp
10 oz (285 g)	WHOLEMEAL FLOUR	1 lb 6 oz (625 g)
	PARSLEY TO GARNISH	

1 Mix all vegetables (apart from beans) and sweat in oil in a large pan.

2 Drain all beans. Add them with the stock and herbs to the vegetables. Bring to boil and simmer 10–15 minutes.

3 Make the dumplings by mixing flour with about 3 fl oz (70 ml) water to make a soft dough. Knead and make into 40 (or 100) small dumplings.

4 Place dumplings in stew and cook further 15 minutes.

5 Serve with boiled potatoes or rice.

NUTRIENT ANALYSIS PER PORTION			
ENERGY (CALORIES)	kcal 496	kJ 2073	MINERALS & VITAMINS IN LARGE AMOUNTS
	GRAMS (g)	AS % TOTAL ENERGY	
TOTAL FAT	6.4	12.0	Potassium,
SATURATED FAT	.8	1.5	iron, zinc
TOTAL CARBOHYDRATE	80.0	60.0	Vitamins A,
ADDED SUGARS	–	–	B group,
PROTEIN	35.0	28.0	C, D, E,
FIBRE	33.0g		folic acid
SALT	2.4g		

FRESH VEGETABLES WITH BROWN RICE *(V)*

Julie Crouch
Milton Keynes

10 portions		25 portions
1½ lb (675 g)	CARROTS	3½ lb (1.5 kg)
12 oz (350 g)	RED PEPPER	1¾ lb (800 g)
12 oz (350 g)	GREEN PEPPER	1¾ lb (800 g)
1½ lb (675 g)	ONIONS	3½ lb (1.5 kg)
1½ lb (675 g)	FIELD (OR BUTTON) MUSHROOMS	3½ lb (1.5 kg)
1 lb (450 g)	BROWN RICE	2½ lb (1.1 kg)
5	LARGE ORANGES	12
	Sauce	
1½ pt (850 ml)	PURE ORANGE JUICE	3½ pt (2 l)
1 tbsp	WORCESTERSHIRE SAUCE	2½ tbsp
1½ lb (675 g)	FIRM TOMATOES	3½ lb (1.5 kg)
1	CUCUMBER	2½
1 tbsp	CORNFLOUR	2½ tbsp

1 Cut carrots into batons. Cook in water or microwave until just firm.
2 Slice peppers, onions and mushrooms into similar size strips. Set aside.
3 Boil rice until cooked.
4 Peel orange in thin strips and set aside. Segment the oranges and squeeze excess juice into a saucepan.
5 Pour about ½ cup (100 ml) pure orange juice into the same saucepan, add Worcestershire sauce, green and red peppers, onions, mushrooms and strips of peel. Cook on high heat until bubbling fast. Turn to minimum heat.
6 Slice tomatoes and cucumber and add them with orange segments to the pan. Turn off heat and cover saucepan with close-fitting lid.
7 Add cornflour to remaining orange juice and mix well. Bring to boil then simmer gently until clear then add to the vegetable mixture and cover with lid.
8 Arrange rice in a ring on plates. Stir vegetables and spoon into centre.

This dish is an excellent starter, but the portions in this recipe are meant for a main course.

NUTRIENT ANALYSIS PER PORTION			
	kcal	kJ	MINERALS &
ENERGY (CALORIES)	289	1208	VITAMINS IN
	GRAMS	AS % TOTAL	LARGE
	(g)	ENERGY	AMOUNTS
TOTAL FAT	2.2	6.8	Potassium,
SATURATED FAT	.5	1.6	calcium,
TOTAL CARBOHYDRATE	63.0	82.0	iron, zinc
ADDED SUGARS	–	–	Vitamins A,
PROTEIN	8.2	11.0	B group,
FIBRE	9.9g		C, E,
SALT	.38g		folic acid

RAINBOW PAELLA *(V,VG)*
Mary Morgan
Leicester

10 portions		25 portions
20 oz (565 g)	POLISHED BROWN RICE	3 lb 4 oz (1.45 kg)
3 lb (1.35 kg)	PREPARED MIXED VEGETABLES. e.g. ONION CUT IN CHUNKS, BABY SWEETCORN, AUBERGINES CUT IN CUBES, CARROTS DICED, BUTTON MUSHROOMS, CAULIFLOWER OR BROCCOLI IN FLORETS, RUNNER BEANS, LARGE PULSES, RED AND GREEN PEPPERS CUT INTO BATONS	
4 oz (115 g)	SOY OR SUNFLOWER OIL	10 oz (285 g)
1/2 pt (300 ml)	VEGETABLE STOCK	2 1/2 pt (1.4 l)
1 oz (30 g)	FRESH PARSLEY, CHOPPED	2 1/2 oz (75 g)
2	LEMONS	4
1	TOMATO, IN WEDGES	3
1/2 oz (15 g)	CRUSHED GARLIC OR PURÉE	2 oz (60 g)
2	BAY LEAVES	4
4 oz (115 g)	FLAKED ALMONDS, TOASTED	10 oz (285 g)
	BLACK PEPPER	
	WATERCRESS TO GARNISH	

1 Cook the rice in boiling water for exactly 15 minutes. Drain and refresh.

2 Sauté onion, aubergine and harder vegetables in oil, stirring frequently until onion begins to brown. Add stock and simmer until vegetables are *al dente*.

3 Add softer vegetables and garlic and continue simmering until all are cooked.

4 Mix rice, cooked vegetables, parsley and juice from half the lemons. Add pepper to taste and pile into serving dishes.

5 Serve garnished with lemon wedges, tomato wedges, almonds and watercress.

This vegetarian dish copies the traditional Spanish paella, which is served with whole prawns and lobster claws still in their shells. Prepare it with courageously large pieces of vegetables. It is almost a dish you could eat with your fingers!

NUTRIENT ANALYSIS PER PORTION			
	kcal	kJ	MINERALS &
ENERGY (CALORIES)	407	1701	VITAMINS IN
	GRAMS	AS % TOTAL	LARGE
	(g)	ENERGY	AMOUNTS
TOTAL FAT	20.0	43.0	Potassium,
SATURATED FAT	2.5	5.6	calcium,
TOTAL CARBOHYDRATE	52.0	48.0	iron, zinc
ADDED SUGARS	–	–	Vitamins A,
PROTEIN	9.0	8.8	B_1, B_2, B_6,
FIBRE	8.4g		nicotinic acid,
SALT	31mg		C, E

BEAN CASSEROLE *(V,VG)*

Mary Deans
Edinburgh

10 portions		25 portions
4	LARGE ONIONS, SLICED	10
2	CLOVES GARLIC, CRUSHED	5
2 tbsp	SOYA OIL	5 tbsp
1 lb (450 g)	COURGETTES	2½ lb (1.5 kg)
2 oz (60 g)	TOMATO PURÉE	5 oz (140 g)
1 pt (570 ml)	WATER	2½ pt (1.5 l)
2 tbsp	CHOPPED PARSLEY	5 tbsp
2 lb (900 g)	READY-COOKED BEANS, ANY TYPE	5 lb (2.3 kg)
¾ lb (350 g)	MUSHROOMS, QUARTERED	1¾ lb (800 g)
1 pt (570 ml)	TOMATO JUICE	2½ pt (1.5 l)
	PEPPER	

1 Sauté onion and garlic in oil until golden brown.
2 Wipe, trim and slice courgettes then add to onion. Cook 5 minutes.
3 Stir in tomato juice and purée, water and parsley. Bring to boil and simmer 10 minutes.
4 Add drained cooked beans and mushrooms. Simmer 10 minutes. Season.
5 Serve hot with vegetables or cold as salad.

NUTRIENT ANALYSIS PER PORTION			
ENERGY (CALORIES)	kcal 170	kJ 711	MINERALS & VITAMINS IN LARGE AMOUNTS
	GRAMS (g)	AS % TOTAL ENERGY	
TOTAL FAT	4.7	25.0	Potassium,
SATURATED FAT	.7	3.7	iron, copper,
TOTAL CARBOHYDRATE	24.0	53.0	zinc
ADDED SUGARS	1.8	4.0	Vitamins C,
PROTEIN	9.2	22.0	folic acid
FIBRE	7.0g		
SALT	.4g		

CHILLI, BEANS & VEGETABLES (V, VG)

Linda Lennison
Cheshire

10 portions		25 portions
1 lb 5 oz (500 g)	DRIED RED KIDNEY BEANS	1 lb 15 oz (1¼ kg)
2¼ lb (1 kg)	CAN BAKED BEANS	6 lb 11 oz (2.6 kg)
2¼ lb (1 kg)	CAN TOMATOES	5 lb 11 oz (2.6 kg)
¾ tsp	CHILLI POWDER	1½ tsp
¾ tsp	GARLIC GRANULES	2 tsp
2	BAY LEAVES	7
1 tsp	DRIED BASIL	3 tsp
1 tsp	MUSTARD	2 tsp
1 tbsp	SOY SAUCE	2 tbsp
1	MEDIUM ONION	4
3½ oz (100 g)	MUSHROOMS	8½ oz (250 g)
1	SMALL GREEN PEPPER	2
2	STICKS CELERY	5
1	LEEK	2

1 Soak the kidney beans for 12 hours, cook them in fresh water and reserve the stock.

2 Add the kidney beans, cans of tomato and of baked beans, the herbs and spices, and the bean stock to a large casserole dish and bring to the boil.

3 Chop the onion, mushrooms, and other vegetables and add them all to the casserole dish. Stir well.

4 Bring to the boil and simmer for 20–30 minutes.

5 Serve with rice or chunks of wholemeal bread.

Even meat eaters couldn't believe there wasn't at least the odd beef stock-cube thrown in. This dish was often requested for buffet menus.

NUTRIENT ANALYSIS PER PORTION			
	kcal	kJ	MINERALS &
ENERGY (CALORIES)	226	945	VITAMINS IN
	GRAMS	AS % TOTAL	LARGE
	(g)	ENERGY	AMOUNTS
TOTAL FAT	1.7	6.7	Potassium,
SATURATED FAT	.3	1.1	calcium, iron,
TOTAL CARBOHYDRATE	37.0	67.0	zinc
ADDED SUGARS	3.4	5.6	Vitamins A,
PROTEIN	18.0	32.0	B_1, B_6, C,
FIBRE	22.0g		nicotinic acid,
SALT	1.34g		folic acid

MILLET & ADUKI PIE
(V, VG)
East West Restaurant
London

10 portions		25 portions
7 oz (200 g)	MILLET	1 lb 2 oz (500 g)
14 oz (400 g)	ADUKI BEANS	2¼ lb (1 kg)
1	HANDFUL ROLLED OATS	2
1	SMALL CAULIFLOWER	3
4½ fl oz (140 ml)	SOYA MILK	12 fl oz (350 ml)
3 oz (90 g)	TAHINI	7½ oz (215 g)
12 oz (350 g)	ONIONS	30 oz (735 g)
	SESAME OIL	
	SHOYU	

Sauce

4 oz (115 g)	ONIONS	10 oz (285 g)
8 oz (225 g)	MUSHROOMS	20 oz (565 g)
4½ fl oz (140 ml)	SOYA MILK	12½ fl oz (350 ml)
	SHOYU	
	ARROWROOT	

1 Cook millet in three times its own volume of water.

2 Cook aduki beans just covered with water and with lid on saucepan. When cooked, stir in the rolled oats to thicken.

3 Cut cauliflower into pieces and boil until just soft. Mash it with soya milk, add tahini and stir into millet.

4 Slice and sauté onions and mix with beans. Line a baking dish with the beans, add the millet mixture brushing top with a mixture of sesame oil and shoyu and bake in hot oven until brown on top.

5 Make the sauce by sautéing the onions and whole mushrooms until cooked, cool and blend with soya milk then season with shoyu. Thicken with a little arrowroot slaked in cold water before adding and bringing to the boil.

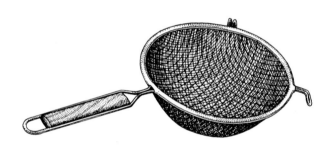

NUTRIENT ANALYSIS PER PORTION			
	kcal	kJ	MINERALS &
ENERGY (CALORIES)	229	957	VITAMINS IN
	GRAMS	AS % TOTAL	LARGE
	(g)	ENERGY	AMOUNTS
TOTAL FAT	7.2	28.0	Potassium,
SATURATED FAT	1.1	4.2	calcium, iron,
TOTAL CARBOHYDRATE	33.0	54.0	zinc
ADDED SUGARS	–	–	Vitamins B$_1$,
PROTEIN	9.5	17.0	B$_2$, B$_6$, C
FIBRE	4.7g		
SALT	58.4mg		

SOMBRERO CHILLI BEANS
(V,VG)

Mary Morgan
Leicester

10 portions		25 portions
12 oz (350 g)	RED KIDNEY BEANS	1 lb 12 oz (800 g)
12 oz (350 g)	PLUM PEELED TOMATOES CHOPPED WITH JUICE	1 lb 12 oz (800 g)
6 oz (170 g)	TOMATO PURÉE	1 lb (450 g)
6 oz (170 g)	CHOPPED GREEN PEPPERS	1 lb (450 g)
	GARLIC CLOVES TO TASTE	
1 dsp	CHILLI POWDER	2.5 dsp

1 Soak beans overnight. Boil until just tender. Drain and refresh.
2 Mix all other ingredients with beans. Bring to boil slowly and serve with rice, pasta or baked potatoes.

A simple recipe with 101 uses. Serve as a simple chilli dish or top with a dollop of guacomole stabbed with tortilla chips for a more fancy presentation. Use it as a pastry or pie filling or serve hot shepherd's-pie style with mashed potato.

NUTRIENT ANALYSIS PER PORTION			
	kcal	kJ	MINERALS & VITAMINS IN LARGE AMOUNTS
ENERGY (CALORIES)	116	485	
	GRAMS (g)	AS % TOTAL ENERGY	
TOTAL FAT	.8	5.8	Potassium,
SATURATED FAT	.1	1.0	zinc
TOTAL CARBOHYDRATE	19.0	62.0	Vitamins B$_1$,
ADDED SUGARS	–	–	C, E
PROTEIN	9.4	33.0	
FIBRE	9.3g		
SALT	83.8mg		

BROWN RICE & BLACK-EYED BEANS *(V,VG)*

Pauline Moore
Douglas
Isle of Man

10 portions		25 portions
12 oz (350 g)	DRIED BLACK-EYED BEANS	30 oz (735 g)
3 pt (1.75 l)	VEGETABLE STOCK	7½ pt (4 l)
3 lb (1.35 kg)	TOMATOES SKINNED AND CHOPPED	7½ lb (3.45 kg)
12 oz (350 g)	BROWN RICE	30 oz (735 g)
pinch	CAYENNE PEPPER	1 tsp
6 tsp	CHOPPED PARSLEY	9 tsp

1 Soak beans overnight, drain and place in a lidded saucepan with the stock. Bring to boil then simmer with lid on for 1 hour or until cooked.

2 Add tomatoes and rice, return to boil and cook on low heat for 20 minutes.

3 Add cayenne and half the parsley, stir and turn into serving dish. Garnish with parsley and serve.

NUTRIENT ANALYSIS PER PORTION			
	kcal	kJ	MINERALS &
ENERGY (CALORIES)	209	874	VITAMINS IN
	GRAMS	AS % TOTAL	LARGE
	(g)	ENERGY	AMOUNTS
TOTAL FAT	1.1	4.7	Potassium,
SATURATED FAT	.4	1.5	iron, zinc
TOTAL CARBOHYDRATE	41.0	74.0	Vitamins A,
ADDED SUGARS	–	–	B₁, B₆,
PROTEIN	10.0	19.0	nicotinic acid,
FIBRE	4.6g		C, E
SALT	1.21g		

LENTIL LASAGNE *(V)*

Mary Deans
Edinburgh

10 portions		25 portions
1 lb (450 g)	BROWN LENTILS	2½ lb (1.1 kg)
2	ONIONS, DICED	5
3 oz (90 g)	POLYUNSATURATED VEGETABLE MARGARINE	8 oz (225 g)
2 pt (1.1 l)	WATER	5 pt (2.85 l)
2 tsp	CORIANDER SEEDS, GROUND	5 tsp
4	EGGS	10
6 oz (170 g)	GRATED LOW-FAT CHEESE	1 lb (450 g)
1½ pt (850 ml)	BÉCHAMEL SAUCE, MADE WITH POLYUNSATURATED VEGETABLE MARGARINE AND SEMI-SKIMMED MILK	4 pt (2.25 ml)
1 lb (450 g)	WHOLEMEAL 'QUICK COOK' LASAGNE	2½ lb (1.1 kg)
	PEPPER TO TASTE	

1 Soak lentils in cold water for at least 2 hours.
2 Sweat onion in margarine.
3 Drain lentils and place with onions in pan, add water and bring to boil. Cover and simmer for 45 minutes, until lentils just soft.
4 Add spice and season to taste.
5 Beat eggs and add with ⅔ of cheese to béchamel sauce.
6 Grease ovenproof dish and, starting with a layer of lentils, make alternate layers of pasta and lentils, finishing with a layer of sauce.
7 Sprinkle cheese on top and bake at 400°F (200°C, gas mark 6) for 40 minutes.

NUTRIENT ANALYSIS PER PORTION			
	kcal	kJ	MINERALS & VITAMINS IN LARGE AMOUNTS
ENERGY (CALORIES)	427	1785	
	GRAMS (g)	AS % TOTAL ENERGY	
TOTAL FAT	18.0	39.0	Potassium,
SATURATED FAT	4.6	9.7	calcium, iron,
TOTAL CARBOHYDRATE	44.0	39.0	zinc
ADDED SUGARS	–	–	Vitamins A,
PROTEIN	24.0	23.0	B_1, B_2, D
FIBRE	7.2g		
SALT	1.6g		

CANNELLONI STUFFED WITH LENTILS *(V)*

Graham Scholey
Watford

10 portions		25 portions
	Filling	
8 oz (225 g)	BROWN LENTILS	1¼ lb (565 g)
2 oz (60 g)	CARROTS	5 oz (140 g)
1	STICK CELERY	3
2 oz (60 g)	ONIONS	5 oz (140 g)
1	VEGETABLE STOCK CUBE	2½
	PINCH CHILLI POWDER	
	BOUQUET GARNI	
½ oz (15 g)	PORRIDGE OATS	2½ oz (75 g)
1¼ lb (565 g)	CANNELLONI TUBES, PRE-COOKED	3 lb (1.35 kg)
	Sauce	
2 oz (60 g)	POLYUNSATURATED VEGETABLE MARGARINE	3 oz (90 g)
4 oz (115 g)	ONION	10 oz (285 g)
1	CLOVE GARLIC	3
4 oz (115 g)	FLOUR	10 oz (285 g)
4 oz (115 g)	TOMATO PURÉE	10 oz (285 g)
2 pt (1.1 l)	VEGETABLE STOCK	5 pt (2.85 l)
¼ pt (150 ml)	WHITE WINE	13 fl oz (380 ml)
1 only	RED PEPPER	1 lb (450 g)
1 only	LEEK	1 lb (450 g)

1 Soak lentils overnight, rinse off. Add to saucepan together with chopped carrots, celery and onion, stock cube, chilli powder and bouquet garni. Cover with water and boil.

2 When lentils are soft, remove bouquet garni, add the oats and simmer for few minutes to thicken. Allow to cool then blend lightly.

3 Pipe mixture into cannelloni tubes.

Sauce

4 Sweat onions and garlic, stir in the flour and make roux. Add tomato purée.

5 Dilute with stock by adding a little at a time. Add the wine and simmer for 20 minutes. Cut red peppers into short julienne strips and the leek into coarser ones. Add them both and remove from heat.

6 Place a little sauce in the bottom of an oven-proof dish. Lay stuffed tubes in single layer. Cover with sauce, reserving some addition when serving. Cook covered in moderate oven 350°F (180°C, gas mark 4) for 30 minutes.

NUTRIENT ANALYSIS PER PORTION			
	kcal	kJ	MINERALS &
ENERGY (CALORIES)	411	1718	VITAMINS IN
	GRAMS	AS % TOTAL	LARGE
	(g)	ENERGY	AMOUNTS
TOTAL FAT	6.6	15.0	Potassium,
SATURATED FAT	1.1	2.5	iron, zinc
TOTAL CARBOHYDRATE	72.0	65.0	Vitamins B_1,
ADDED SUGARS	–	–	C, E
PROTEIN	18.0	18.0	
FIBRE	5.7g		
SALT	1.16g		

WHOLEMEAL PITTA BREAD PIZZA *(V)*

Rivers L W
Oxford

10 portions		25 portions
10	WHOLEMEAL PITTA BREAD	25
2 lb (900 g)	CANNED CHOPPED TOMATOES	5 lb (2.4 kg)
10 tsp	OREGANO, DRIED	25 tsp
10 oz (285 g)	EDAM, SLICED THINLY	1 lb 6 oz (610 g)
	PEPPER	

1 Place pitta breads on baking sheet and cover each with chopped tomatoes. Sprinkle 1 tsp oregano on each and top with slices of cheese.
2 Bake for 15–20 minutes at 375°F (190°C, gas mark 5).

NUTRIENT ANALYSIS PER PORTION			
	kcal	kJ	MINERALS &
ENERGY (CALORIES)	270	1129	VITAMINS IN
	GRAMS	AS % TOTAL	LARGE
	(g)	ENERGY	AMOUNTS
TOTAL FAT	7.4	25.0	Potassium,
SATURATED FAT	4.5	15.0	iron, zinc
TOTAL CARBOHYDRATE	39.0	54.0	Vitamins
ADDED SUGARS	–	–	A, B_1, C, E,
PROTEIN	15.0	22.0	
FIBRE	5.1g		
SALT	1.6g		

CROQUETTES OF MILLET WITH RED PEPPER SAUCE (V)

Jean-Claude Juston
London

10 portions		25 portions
2½ lb (1.1 kg)	MILLET	7½ lb (3.45 kg)
2 lb (900 g)	ONIONS	5 lb (2.45 kg)
3	GARLIC	7
½	HANDFUL FRESH HERBS (SORREL, SAGE)	1
1 lb (450 g)	SHELLED GREEN PEAS	3 lb (1.35 kg)
1 lb (450 g)	CHEDDAR, GRATED (OPTIONAL)	2½ (1.1 kg)
	WALNUT HALVES FOR DECORATION	
	BLACK PEPPER TO TASTE	
	Sauce	
1 lb (450 g)	LIGHT ROUX MADE WITH SOYA OIL OR POLYUNSATURATED VEGETABLE OIL MARGARINE	2½ lb (1.1 kg)
2	RED PEPPERS	5
8 fl oz (250 ml)	VEGETABLE STOCK	20 fl oz (570 ml)
2 pt (1.1 l)	WATER	5 pt (2.85 l)

1 Bring millet to boil just covered in water. Simmer until almost cooked, remove lid to evaporate liquid. Let cool.

2 Chop onions and garlic and sweat with most of the chopped fresh herbs (dried can be used). Add peas, stir and remove from heat.

3 Mix in millet (and grated cheese if used) and shape into croquettes. Top with walnut halves. Bake 15 minutes at 400°F (200°C, gas mark 6).

4 Make a light roux. Mix red pepper with vegetable stock in blender add slowly the liquid to the roux on a gentle heat, stirring to form a smooth sauce. Cover croquettes with sauce and garnish with chopped herbs. Serve hot.

NUTRIENT ANALYSIS PER PORTION			
	kcal	kJ	MINERALS & VITAMINS IN LARGE AMOUNTS
ENERGY (CALORIES)	669	2796	
	GRAMS (g)	AS % TOTAL ENERGY	
TOTAL FAT	24.0	32.0	Potassium,
SATURATED FAT	11.2	15.0	calcium,
TOTAL CARBOHYDRATE	91.0	51.0	iron, zinc
ADDED SUGARS	–	–	Vitamins A,
PROTEIN	28.0	17.0	B group,
FIBRE	7.4g		C, E
SALT	1.3g		

LENTIL BURGERS *(V)*

Angela Jacas
London

10 portions		25 portions
1 lb 2 oz (529 g)	BROWN LENTILS	2 lb 14 oz (1.25 kg)
6 oz (170 g)	WHITE CABBAGE, FINELY CHOPPED	1 lb (450 g)
6 oz (170 g)	ONION, DICED	1 lb (450 g)
6 oz (170 g)	WHOLEMEAL BREADCRUMBS	1 lb (450 g)
½ tsp	DRIED MIXED HERBS	1½ tsp
3	EGGS	8
	SOYA OIL	

1 Cook lentils until soft and drain.
2 Mix all ingredients together and shape into burgers.
3 Toss in extra breadcrumbs and lightly shallow fry 3–4 minutes each side in soya oil.

NUTRIENT ANALYSIS PER PORTION			
	kcal	kJ	MINERALS & VITAMINS IN LARGE AMOUNTS
ENERGY (CALORIES)	231	966	
	GRAMS (g)	AS % TOTAL ENERGY	
TOTAL FAT	2.9	11.0	Potassium,
SATURATED FAT	.77	3.0	iron, zinc
TOTAL CARBOHYDRATE	37.0	60.0	Vitamins
ADDED SUGARS	–	–	B_1, B_6
PROTEIN	17.0	29.0	
FIBRE	8.40g		
SALT	.39g		

LENTIL BURGERS WITH YOGHURT SAUCE *(V)*

Miss H. B. Yeulett
Sussex

10 portions		25 portions
15 oz (430 g)	SPLIT RED LENTILS	1 lb 5 oz (590 g)
1 pt 17½ fl oz (1.1 l)	STOCK	4 pt 14 fl oz (2.4 l)
2½	SMALL ONIONS, CHOPPED	6

3	BAY LEAVES	7
1¼ tsp	CUMIN, GROUND	3½ tsp
5	MEDIUM TOMATOES, SKINNED AND CHOPPED	13
10 oz (285 g)	UNSALTED PEANUTS, CHOPPED	25 oz (705 g)
5 tbsp	BRAN	12 tbsp
8 oz (225 g)	WHOLEMEAL BREADCRUMBS	20 oz (550 g)
5 tbsp	PARSLEY, CHOPPED	13 tbsp
3	EGGS, BEATEN	7
	BLACK PEPPER	

Sauce

1¼ pt (700 ml)	NATURAL YOGHURT	3¼ pt (1.8 l)
5 tbsp	CHOPPED CHIVES	13 tbsp
2 cloves	GARLIC	5 cloves
2	LEMON RINDS	5

1 Put lentils in pan with stock, onion, bay leaves, cumin, tomatoes. Bring to boil and simmer until lentils are soft.

2 Remove bay leaves, beat lentil purée until smooth.

3 Heat oven to 375°F (190°C, gas mark 5).

4 Mix peanuts, bran and breadcrumbs. Beat half this mixture into lentil purée. Season and stir in parsley.

5 Bind with beaten egg. Divide into flat cakes and place them on greased baking sheet. Coat with remainder of the breadcrumbs mix. Bake for 20–25 minutes.

6 Make sauce by mixing all sauce ingredients together and season with pepper.

NUTRIENT ANALYSIS PER PORTION			
ENERGY (CALORIES)	kcal 505	kJ 2111	MINERALS & VITAMINS IN LARGE AMOUNTS
	GRAMS (g)	AS % TOTAL ENERGY	
TOTAL FAT	20.0	36.0	Potassium,
SATURATED FAT	4.55	8.10	calcium,
TOTAL CARBOHYDRATE	51.0	38.0	iron
ADDED SUGARS	–	–	Vitamins A,
PROTEIN	23.0	36.0	B group, C,
FIBRE	16.0g		folic acid
SALT	1.06g		

VEGETABLE & CHICK PEA CASSEROLE (V, VG)

Angela Jacas
London

10 portions		25 portions
1 lb 2 oz (520 g)	CHICK PEAS	2 lb 14 oz (1.25 kg)
1	LARGE ONION	2½
6	PARSLEY SPRIGS	12
3 tbsp	SOY OIL	8 tbsp
3	CLOVES GARLIC	6
6	STICKS CELERY	1 bnch
3	CARROTS	8
1½	RED PEPPERS	4
3 tsp	CORIANDER SEEDS, CRUSHED	8 tsp
1 lb 2 oz (520 g)	TIN TOMATOES	2 lb 14 oz (1.25 kg)
1½ pt	MARMITE STOCK	3¾ pt
3 tbsp	FRESH CORIANDER LEAVES, CHOPPED	8 tbsp
	PEPPER	

1 Soak chick peas overnight.

2 Drain chick peas. Put in pan with onion and parsley sprigs, cover with water and boil. Simmer for 2 hours or until peas tender. Drain.

3 Heat oil and fry garlic, celery, carrots and red pepper lightly for 4 minutes stirring frequently. Add crushed coriander seeds and cook 1 minute.

4 Add tomatoes, stock, pea mixture with half the chopped coriander and bring to the boil stirring well. Cover and cook in slow oven for 2 hours.

5 Correct seasoning, garnish with remainder of herbs and serve hot.

NUTRIENT ANALYSIS PER PORTION			
	kcal	kJ	MINERALS & VITAMINS IN LARGE AMOUNTS
ENERGY (CALORIES)	124	518	
	GRAMS (g)	AS % TOTAL ENERGY	
TOTAL FAT	8.4	61.0	Potassium,
SATURATED FAT	1.8	13.0	iron
TOTAL CARBOHYDRATE	8.3	25.0	Vitamins
ADDED SUGARS	–	–	A, C
PROTEIN	4.3	14.0	
FIBRE	4.5g		
SALT	.83g		

LASAGNE FLORENTINE (V)

Judith Liddel
Aberdeen

10 portions		25 portions
9 oz (255 g)	ONION, CHOPPED	1 lb 6 oz (675 g)
2.5 lb (1.13 kg)	CANNED TOMATOES	6.5 lb (3 kg)
1 oz (30 g)	TOMATO PURÉE	2.5 oz (75 g)
2 tsp	DRIED BASIL	5 tsp
1 tsp	DRIED THYME	2.5 tsp
	BLACK PEPPER	
1.25 pt (725 ml)	SKIMMED MILK	3 pt (1.75 l)
5 oz (140 g)	WHOLEMEAL FLOUR	12 oz (350 g)
5 lb (2.3 kg)	FRESH SPINACH, CHOPPED AND STEAMED	12 lb 8 oz (5.7 kg)
1 lb 3 oz (535 g)	WHOLEMEAL NO PRE-COOK LASAGNE	3 lb (1.35 kg)
1 lb (450 g)	CHEDDAR, GRATED	2 lb 8 oz (1.15 kg)

1 Place onion, tomatoes, purée, herbs and pepper in a pan and simmer for 10 minutes.

2 Make a sauce by adding some milk to flour to form a thin paste. Heat, slowly adding rest of milk. Boil and simmer until cooked. Add spinach and stir.

3 Dip lasagne sheets in water. Spread a third of the sauce on the bottom of a baking tin. Cover with a layer of lasagne, a layer of sauce and some cheese. Repeat layering finishing with a layer of cheese. Bake at 350°F (180°C, gas mark 4) for 40 minutes.

NUTRIENT ANALYSIS PER PORTION			
	kcal	kJ	MINERALS &
ENERGY (CALORIES)	510	2132	VITAMINS IN
	GRAMS	AS % TOTAL	LARGE
	(g)	ENERGY	AMOUNTS
TOTAL FAT	19.0	33.0	Potassium,
SATURATED FAT	10.2	18.0	iron, zinc
TOTAL CARBOHYDRATE	60.0	44.0	Vitamins A,
ADDED SUGARS	–	–	B group,
PROTEIN	29.9	23.0	C, E,
FIBRE	9.5g		folic acid
SALT	1.23g		

MARINATED MUSHROOMS
(V, VG)

Compass
London

10 portions		25 portions
2 lb 8 oz (1.1 kg)	MUSHROOMS, BUTTON	6 lb 4 oz (2.8 kg)
5 tbsp	SOYA OIL	12 tbsp
3 tsp	CORIANDER SEEDS, GROUND	7 tsp
2	BAY LEAVES	5
	GARLIC CLOVES TO TASTE	
5 tbsp	LEMON JUICE	12 tbsp
	BLACK PEPPER TO TASTE	

1 Wash mushrooms and fry in oil with coriander, bay leaves and garlic for 2 minutes.

2 Tip mushrooms into large bowl. Add lemon juice and pepper. Chill before serving.

NUTRIENT ANALYSIS PER PORTION			
ENERGY (CALORIES)	kcal 83	kJ 347	MINERALS & VITAMINS IN
	GRAMS (g)	AS % TOTAL ENERGY	LARGE AMOUNTS
TOTAL FAT	8.2	88.0	Potassium
SATURATED FAT	1.2	13.0	Vitamins B_2,
TOTAL CARBOHYDRATE	.4	1.7	nicotinic acid
ADDED SUGARS	–	–	
PROTEIN	2.0	9.8	
FIBRE	2.8g		
SALT	25.4mg		

CHEESE & POTATO PIE (V)

Linda Lennison
Cheshire

10 portions		25 portions
4 lb (1.8 kg)	POTATOES	10 lb (4.5 kg)
1 oz (30 g)	SUNFLOWER MARGARINE	3 oz (90 g)
1	EGG	2
14 oz (400 g)	LOW-FAT CHEDDAR CHEESE	2¼ lb (1 kg)
	WHITE PEPPER	

1 Peel and boil the potatoes then mash them with the margarine and egg. Season.

2 Spread half the potato evenly over the bottom of a greased dish and sprinkle the cheese on top.

3 Spread the remaining potato on top, decorate it with patterns made with a fork, then brown under a grill or in the oven.

4 Serve hot or chilled with green salads, other vegetables or chilli beans and vegetables (p. 159).

The proportions of cheese and potato are important. Too much cheese runs out on reheating, too little and the potato taste dominates. The dish is very cheap and was very popular from the day it was introduced in the restaurant.

NUTRIENT ANALYSIS PER PORTION			
ENERGY (CALORIES)	kcal 213	kJ 890	MINERALS & VITAMINS IN
	GRAMS (g)	AS % TOTAL ENERGY	LARGE AMOUNTS
TOTAL FAT	17.0	45.0	Potassium,
SATURATED FAT	9.2	24.0	calcium,
TOTAL CARBOHYDRATE	35.0	39.0	zinc
ADDED SUGARS	–	–	Vitamins A,
PROTEIN	14.0	17.0	B_6, B_{12}, C
FIBRE	1.8g		
SALT	.74g		

VEGAN VEGETABLE LASAGNE *(V,VG)*

Shirlee Posner
London

10 portions		25 portions
1 pkt	RECORD NO-PRE-COOK LASAGNE	2 pkt
	Sauce	
1 lb (450 g)	CARROTS, SLICED THINLY	2½ lb (1.1 kg)
2	GARLIC, CLOVES	5
1 lb (450 g)	ONIONS, SLICED	2½ lb (1.1 kg)
3 oz (90 g)	SOY/SUNFLOWER OIL	8 oz (225 g)
½ A10 (3 kg)	TIN TOMATOES	1½ A10 (4.5 kg)
2 tbsp	TOMATO PURÉE	6 tbsp
	OREGANO	

White sauce

3 oz (90 g)	PLAIN FLOUR	8 oz (225 g)
2 pt (1.1 l)	SOY MILK	5 pt (2.85 l)
1/4 oz (7.5 g)	MARIGOLD OR FIGGS BOUILLON	1/2 oz (15 g)
2 oz (60 g)	PEANUT BUTTER (SMOOTH)	5 oz (140 g)

Vegetables

1½ lb (675 g)	MIXTURE OF ANY OF AUBERGINES, PEPPERS, COURGETTES, CARROTS, PARSNIPS, SWEDES, POTATO, FENNEL ACCORDING TO SEASON AND BUDGET	2 lb 4 oz (1 kg)

1 Fry carrots, garlic and onions in as little soy oil as possible.
2 Add tomatoes, tomato purée and oregano and simmer gently for 20 minutes.
3 Make the white sauce starting with a roux, adding the milk and then stirring in the bouillon and peanut butter.
4 Chop vegetables finely and mix.
5 Place a layer of tomato sauce in bottom of oven-proof dish. Lay single layer of pasta on which place a layer of finely chopped mixed vegetables. Cover with layer of sauce. Repeat series of layers to top of dish, ending with a layer of tomato sauce, top with white sauce. Bake at 350°F (180°C, gas mark 4) for 30–40 minutes.

NUTRIENT ANALYSIS PER PORTION			
	kcal	kJ	MINERALS &
ENERGY (CALORIES)	439	1835	VITAMINS IN
	GRAMS	AS % TOTAL	LARGE
	(g)	ENERGY	AMOUNTS
TOTAL FAT	16	34	Potassium,
SATURATED FAT	2.6	5.3	calcium,
TOTAL CARBOHYDRATE	62.0	53.0	iron, zinc
ADDED SUGARS	.4	.3	Vitamins A,
PROTEIN	15.0	13.0	B group,
FIBRE	8.7g		C, E,
SALT	.54g		folic acid

VEGETABLE LASAGNE (V)

Elspeth Japp
Aberdeen

10 portions		25 portions
10 oz (285 g)	BROWN LENTILS	25 oz (705 g)
10 oz (285 g)	WHOLEMEAL LASAGNE	25 oz (705 g)
2½ oz (75 g)	POLYUNSATURATED VEGETABLE MARGARINE	6 oz (170 g)

2½ oz (75 g)	WHOLEMEAL FLOUR	6 oz (170 g)
2 pt (1.1 l)	SKIMMED MILK	5 pt (2.8 l)
5	EGGS, BEATEN	12
¼ tsp	GRATED NUTMEG	½ tsp
	Sauce	
2 tbsp	SUNFLOWER OIL	6 tbsp
2	ONIONS, CHOPPED	6
2 cloves	GARLIC, CRUSHED	6 cloves
35 oz (1 kg)	CANNED TOMATOES	90 oz (2.6 kg)
2 tbsp	TOMATO PURÉE	6 tbsp
4 tsp	DRIED OREGANO	12 tsp
	BLACK PEPPER	

1 Cook lentils in boiling water until soft, 25–50 minutes. Drain.

2 Make sauce by sweating onions and garlic in the oil for 3 minutes, adding tomatoes and bringing to the boil. Simmer for 30 minutes to thicken sauce. Add purée then the lentils. Stir in the oregano.

3 Grease an ovenproof dish. Place a layer of sauce in the bottom then add alternate layers of pasta sheets and sauce making sure the top sheets of pasta are completely covered with sauce.

4 Heat the margarine in a pan. Add the wholemeal flour while stirring. Heat for three minutes then slowly add the milk while stirring continuously. Slowly add the beaten eggs then the nutmeg and pepper to taste. Pour over lasagne.

5 Bake at 350°F (180°C, gas mark 4) for 40 minutes.

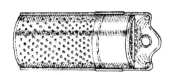

NUTRIENT ANALYSIS PER PORTION			
	kcal	kJ	MINERALS &
ENERGY (CALORIES)	355	1484	VITAMINS IN
	GRAMS	AS % TOTAL	LARGE
	(g)	ENERGY	AMOUNTS
TOTAL FAT	13.0	33.0	Potassium,
SATURATED FAT	2.6	6.7	calcium,
TOTAL CARBOHYDRATE	43.0	46.0	iron, copper,
ADDED SUGARS	–	–	zinc
PROTEIN	19.0	21.0	Vitamins A,
FIBRE	7.1g		B group,
SALT	.47g		folic acid

FRUIT & VEGETABLE CURRY (V, VG)

Pauline Moore
Douglas, Isle of Man

10 portions		25 portions
12	STALKS CELERY, CHOPPED	30
3	ONIONS, CHOPPED	7
3 tbsp	SUNFLOWER OIL	7 tbsp
2 tbsp	CURRY POWDER	5 tbsp
3 tbsp	BARLEY FLOUR	7½ tbsp
1½ pt (850 ml)	VEGETABLE STOCK	3½ pt (2 l)
3 tsp	GRATED FRESH GINGER ROOT	7
2	LEMONS, JUICE AND ZEST	5
12 oz (350 g)	DRIED APRICOT, CHOPPED	30 oz (850 g)
6	BANANAS, THICKLY SLICED	15
3 lb (1.35 kg)	COOKING APPLES, CORED AND PEELED	7½ lb (3.45 kg)
12 oz (350 g)	RAISINS	30 oz (850 g)
	YOGHURT	

1 Sweat the celery and onion in oil. Stir in curry powder and flour over a low heat.

2 Add stock, stirring and bring to the boil. Add ginger, lemon juice and zest, and fruit. Simmer gently until fruit is soft (about 10 minutes).

3 Stir in some yoghurt and serve with rice or baked jacket potatoes.

NUTRIENT ANALYSIS PER PORTION			
	kcal	kJ	MINERALS &
ENERGY (CALORIES)	360	1505	VITAMINS IN
	GRAMS	AS % TOTAL	LARGE
	(g)	ENERGY	AMOUNTS
TOTAL FAT	6.5	16.0	Potassium,
SATURATED FAT	1.0	2.4	calcium,
TOTAL CARBOHYDRATE	74.0	77.0	iron
ADDED SUGARS	–	–	Vitamins
PROTEIN	6.4	7.1	A, B$_6$,
FIBRE	19.0g		nicotinic acid,
SALT	.86g		C, E

Opposite: *Veal Scallops with Cucumber and Peaches p. 151, Minted Cous-cous Filled Tomatoes p. 100.*

Over Page: *Crispy Pasta Casserole p. 133, Tandoori Chicken p. 143, Haddock and Leek Potatoes p. 131.*

CHEESE & BROCCOLI FLAN (V)

Compass, London

10 portions		25 portions
	Pastry	
5 oz (140 g)	POLYUNSATURATED VEGETABLE MARGARINE	12 oz (350 g)
5 oz (140 g)	WHOLEMEAL FLOUR	12 oz (350 g)
5 oz (140 g)	PLAIN FLOUR	12 oz (350 g)
	WATER TO BIND	
	Filling	
1 lb 4 oz (565 g)	BROCCOLI	3 lb 2 oz (1.41 kg)
3	EGGS, BEATEN	8
1 pt 5 fl oz (700 ml)	SKIMMED MILK	3 pt 5 fl oz (1.8 l)
10 oz (285 g)	LOW-FAT CHEESE	1 lb 8 oz (675 g)
2 tsp	DRY MUSTARD	5 tsp
	MIXED HERBS TO TASTE	

1 Make a shortcrust pastry by rubbing fat into mixed flours until it resembles fine breadcrumbs. Add water to make a firm dough.

2 Line a flan tin and chill for 20 minutes. Bake blind at 400°F (200°C, gas mark 6) for 10 minutes.

3 Boil broccoli in a little water for 5–6 minutes. Drain and chop roughly.

4 Beat eggs and mix with milk, three-quarters of the cheese, mustard and herbs.

5 Arrange broccoli in flan case, pour in egg mixture, sprinkle with remaining cheese and return to oven for 25 minutes until set and golden brown.

NUTRIENT ANALYSIS PER PORTION			
	kcal	kJ	MINERALS & VITAMINS IN LARGE AMOUNTS
ENERGY (CALORIES)	293	1225	
	GRAMS (g)	AS % TOTAL ENERGY	
TOTAL FAT	15.0	47.0	Potassium,
SATURATED FAT	3.6	1.0	calcium,
TOTAL CARBOHYDRATE	26.0	34.0	iron, zinc
ADDED SUGARS	–	–	Vitamins A,
PROTEIN	14.0	19.0	B_2, B_{12},
FIBRE	3.8g		C, D, E,
SALT	.79g		folic acid

Previous Page: *Rainbow Paella p. 157, Carrot and Orange Soup p. 110, Blackcurrant and Yoghurt Ice p. 200.*

Opposite: *Cheese and Broccoli Flan p. 177, Turkey, Sweetcorn and Mushroom Pie p. 149, Tomato Salad.*

SPINACH & BROCCOLI BAKE *(V)*

Chris Gray
Southsea

10 portions		25 portions
1 lb 4 oz (565 g)	BROCCOLI, FROZEN	3 lb 12 oz (1.6 kg)
2 lb 8 oz (1.1 kg)	SPINACH, FROZEN	6 lb 4 oz (2.8 kg)
1 lb 4 oz (565 g)	TAGLIATELLE, WHOLEMEAL	3 lb 4 oz (1.5 kg)
2 oz (60 g)	POLYUNSATURATED VEGETABLE MARGARINE	5 oz (140 g)
2 oz (60 g)	PLAIN FLOUR	5 oz (140 g)
1½ pt (850 ml)	SEMI-SKIMMED MILK	3¾ pt (2.2 l)
8 oz (225 g)	BUTTON MUSHROOMS, SLICED	1 lb 4 oz (565 g)
12 oz (350 g)	EDAM CHEESE, GRATED	1 lb (450 g)
5 oz (140 g)	WHOLEMEAL BREADCRUMBS, FRESH	12½ oz (365 g)
½ tsp	DRIED OREGANO	3¾ tsp
	PEPPER	

1 Lightly grease an ovenproof dish. Blanch broccoli for 5 minutes, drain and refresh in cold water. Drain.

2 Cook spinach in a closed pan with a little water. Drain and squeeze out excess water.

3 Boil tagliatelle until *al dente*. Drain.

4 Make a roux with margarine, flour and add the milk slowly on low heat. Add mushrooms and pepper. Simmer for 5 minutes.

5 Spread spinach on base of ovenproof dish. Stir broccoli and tagliatelle into the sauce with half the cheese and spoon over spinach. Sprinkle with herbs and breadcrumbs and remaining cheese. Bake at 375°F (190°C, gas mark 5) for 30–35 minutes or until golden on top.

NUTRIENT ANALYSIS PER PORTION			
	kcal	kJ	MINERALS & VITAMINS IN LARGE AMOUNTS
ENERGY (CALORIES)	497	2077	
	GRAMS (g)	AS % TOTAL ENERGY	
TOTAL FAT	17.0	31.0	Potassium,
SATURATED FAT	7.2	13.0	iron, zinc
TOTAL CARBOHYDRATE	64.0	49.0	Vitamins A,
ADDED SUGARS	–	–	B group,
PROTEIN	26.0	21.0	C, D, E,
FIBRE	6.4g		folic acid
SALT	1.52g		

SPROUT & NUT PIE *(V)*

Linda Lennison
Cheshire

10 portions		25 portions
1¼ lb (565 g)	BRUSSELS SPROUTS	3 lb (1.35 kg)
12 oz (350 g)	RAW PEANUTS	1 lb 12 oz (800 g)
3	STICKS CELERY	1 bunch celery
1	LARGE ONION	2
2 tbsp	CHOPPED PARSLEY	5 tbsp
2 tsp	DRIED THYME	3 tsp
1	GRATED RIND OF LEMON	2
	GROUND BLACK PEPPER	
1 lb (450 g)	PASTRY MADE WITH ½ WHOLEMEAL AND ½ WHITE FLOUR AND 8 OZ SOLID VEGETABLE FAT	2 lb (900 g)
	MILK OR EGG FOR GLAZE	

1 Remove any yellow leaves from sprouts and cook in small amount of boiling water. Reserve cooking water.
2 Place peanuts in a blender, cover with sprout water and blend till smooth.
3 Finely chop celery and dice onion.
4 Mash the sprouts and stir in all other ingredients.
5 Add the blended peanuts, mixing well.
6 Pack mixture into a greased pie dish and top with rolled pastry and glaze.
7 Bake in pre-heated oven at 375°F (190°C, gas mark 5) for 25–30 minutes.
8 Serve with other vegetables or salads.

The dish was created for Christmas menus but became so popular that it was presented throughout the year. Freezes well and can be reheated in a microwave.

NUTRIENT ANALYSIS PER PORTION			
	kcal	kJ	MINERALS & VITAMINS IN LARGE AMOUNTS
ENERGY (CALORIES)	424	1772	
	GRAMS (g)	AS % TOTAL ENERGY	
TOTAL FAT	30.0	63.0	Potassium,
SATURATED FAT	6.2	13.0	iron, zinc
TOTAL CARBOHYDRATE	27.0	34.0	Vitamins
ADDED SUGARS	–	–	B_1, B_6,
PROTEIN	14.0	13.0	nicotinic acid,
FIBRE	6.6g		C, E,
SALT	.52g		folic acid

WHOLEMEAL APPLE PASTIES *(V)*

Mrs Lynn Taylor
Scarborough

10 portions		25 portions
4 oz (115 g)	WHOLEMEAL FLOUR	10½ oz (300 g)
4 oz (115 g)	PLAIN FLOUR	10½ oz (300 g)
4 oz (115 g)	POLYUNSATURATED VEGETABLE MARGARINE	10½ oz (300 g)
	Filling	
1	STICK CELERY	2–3
7 oz (200 g)	CHEESE, CUT INTO ½ IN (1.5 CM) CUBES	1 lb 2 oz (510 g)
8 oz (225 g)	COOKING APPLES, PEELED AND GRATED	20 oz (565 g)
1 tsp	MUSTARD	2
	PEPPER	
	EGG WASH	

1 Make pastry by rubbing margarine into flour until mixture resembles breadcrumbs, then adding water and mixing to a firm dough. Wrap and place in fridge to rest.

2 Wash and chop celery. Mix with apple, cheese, mustard and pepper.

3 Divide pastry into 10 (or 25) pieces and roll each into a circle 6 in (15 cm) across.

4 Divide filling between circles. Dampen edges and fold in half, pressing edges together to seal. Flute edge by pressing between thumb and index-finger. Brush with egg wash.

5 Bake in centre of pre-heated oven at 400°F (200°C, gas mark 6) for 20–25 minutes until golden brown.

NUTRIENT ANALYSIS PER PORTION			
	kcal	kJ	MINERALS & VITAMINS IN LARGE AMOUNTS
ENERGY (CALORIES)	235	982	
	GRAMS (g)	AS % TOTAL ENERGY	
TOTAL FAT	14.0	55.0	Zinc
SATURATED FAT	4.7	18.0	Vitamins
TOTAL CARBOHYDRATE	20.0	31.0	A, C, E
ADDED SUGARS	–	–	
PROTEIN	8.1	14.0	
FIBRE	2.6g		
SALT	.77g		

CHEESE & TOMATO WHOLEMEAL PIZZA (V)

Mrs Beverley Seward
Skipton

10 portions		25 portions
4½ oz (125 g)	WHOLEMEAL FLOUR	11 oz (325 g)
4½ oz (125 g)	PLAIN FLOUR	11 oz (325 g)
⅓ oz (10 g)	BAKING POWDER	1 oz (30 g)
3½ oz (100 g)	POLYUNSATURATED VEGETABLE MARGARINE	11 oz (325 g)
	Topping	
1	ONION	3
1 lb 4 oz (625 g)	CANNED TOMATOES	3 lb 2 oz (1.4 kg)
	MIXED DRIED HERBS	
10½ oz (300 g)	LOW-FAT CHEDDAR, GRATED	1 lb 10 oz (735 g)

1 Mix together flour and baking powder. Rub in margarine and add water to make a soft dough. Roll out thinly and place on a greased baking sheet.

2 Chop and sweat off onion. Add tomatoes and herbs, simmer until it thickens slightly.

3 Spread tomato mixture over dough, sprinkle with cheese and bake at 375°F (190°C, gas mark 5) for 35–40 minutes.

NUTRIENT ANALYSIS PER PORTION			
ENERGY (CALORIES)	kcal 259	kJ 1083	MINERALS & VITAMINS IN LARGE AMOUNTS
	GRAMS (g)	AS % TOTAL ENERGY	
TOTAL FAT	15.0	54.0	Zinc
SATURATED FAT	6.0	21.0	Vitamins
TOTAL CARBOHYDRATE	20.0	30.0	A, C, E
ADDED SUGARS	–	–	
PROTEIN	11.0	17.0	
FIBRE	2.3g		
SALT	1.0g		

DESSERTS

COMPOTE OF DRIED FRUIT IN APPLE JUICE *(V,VG)*

Judith Liddel
Aberdeen

10 portions		25 portions
8 oz (225 g)	DRIED APPLE	1 lb 4 oz (550 g)
8 oz (225 g)	DRIED APRICOT	1 lb 4 oz (550 g)
8 oz (225 g)	PRUNES, DESTONED	1 lb 4 oz (550 g)
4 oz (115 g)	RAISINS	10 oz (285 g)
4 oz (115 g)	SULTANAS	10 oz (285 g)
2 pt (1.1 l)	APPLE JUICE	5 pt (2.8 l)
2	LEMON RINDS	5
	CINNAMON STICK	

1 Soak fruit in apple juice with cinnamon stick and thinly pared lemon rind.
2 Simmer all ingredients for 15 minutes. Remove cinnamon. Serve hot or cold.

NUTRIENT ANALYSIS PER PORTION			
	kcal	kJ	MINERALS & VITAMINS IN LARGE AMOUNTS
ENERGY (CALORIES)	229	957	
	GRAMS (g)	AS % TOTAL ENERGY	
TOTAL FAT	–	–	Potassium,
SATURATED FAT	–	–	iron
TOTAL CARBOHYDRATE	59.0	97.0	Vitamin A
ADDED SUGARS	1.2	2.0	
PROTEIN	2.1	3.7	
FIBRE	11.0g		
SALT	78.7mg		

HOT FRUIT *(V,VG)*

Compass
London

10 portions		25 portions
1 lb 4 oz (565 g)	ORANGES, PEELED	3 lb 4 oz (1.45 kg)
1 lb (450 g)	APPLES, CORED	2 lb 8 oz (1.1 kg)
8 oz (225 g)	BANANAS	1 lb 4 oz (565 g)
4 oz (115 g)	DRIED APRICOTS, SOAKED	8 oz (225 g)
1 pt 5 fl oz (700 ml)	PURE ORANGE JUICE	3 pt 5 fl oz (1.8 l)

1 Slice oranges, apples and bananas. Place in casserole and add apricots and fruit juice.
2 Bake, covered, at 400°F (200°C, gas mark 6) for 20 minutes or until fruit soft. Serve hot.

NUTRIENT ANALYSIS PER PORTION			
	kcal	kJ	MINERALS & VITAMINS IN LARGE AMOUNTS
ENERGY (CALORIES)	96	401	
	GRAMS (g)	AS % TOTAL ENERGY	
TOTAL FAT	.1	.5	Potassium
SATURATED FAT	.1	.3	Vitamin C
TOTAL CARBOHYDRATE	24.0	92.0	
ADDED SUGARS	—	—	
PROTEIN	1.7	7.1	
FIBRE	5.0g		
SALT	27.9mg		

POACHED PEARS IN BLACKCURRANT SAUCE *(V)*

Judith Liddel
Aberdeen

10 portions		25 portions
5	FRESH PEARS	13
	CINNAMON STICK	
12 oz (350 g)	FRESH BLACKCURRANTS	2 lb (900 g)
2 tsp	ARROWROOT	5 tsp
15 fl oz (450 g)	LOW-FAT NATURAL YOGHURT	1¾ pt (1 l)
1 oz (30 g)	FLAKED ALMONDS	2.5 oz (75 g)

1 Poach pear halves in a little water with cinnamon stick. Cool.

2 Liquidise blackcurrants and thicken with arrowroot by bringing to the boil in a pan. Cool.

3 Pour blackcurrants over pears and serve covered with yoghurt and sprinkled with almonds.

NUTRIENT ANALYSIS PER PORTION			
ENERGY (CALORIES)	kcal 70 GRAMS (g)	kJ 293 AS % TOTAL ENERGY	MINERALS & VITAMINS IN LARGE AMOUNTS
TOTAL FAT	2.1	26.0	Potassium
SATURATED FAT	.4	5.0	Vitamin C
TOTAL CARBOHYDRATE	10.0	56.0	
ADDED SUGARS	–	–	
PROTEIN	3.2	18.0	
FIBRE	4.5g		
SALT	91.4mg		

PAULINE'S PIE *(V,VG)*

Pauline Moore
Douglas
Isle of Man

10 portions		25 portions
	Crumble mix	
12 oz (350 g)	OATS	*30 oz (735 g)*
2 oz (60 g)	BROWN RICE FLOUR	*5 oz (140 g)*
1 tbsp	CINNAMON	*2½ tbsp*
4 tbsp	SUNFLOWER OIL	*10 tbsp*
4 tbsp	APPLE JUICE	*10 tbsp*
	Filling	
5	APPLES	*13*
5	PEARS	*13*
2 tbsp	BLACKBERRIES	*5 tbsp*
2 tbsp	APPLE JUICE	*5 tbsp*

Sauce

4 tbsp	SOYA FLOUR	10 tbsp
2 pt (1.1 l)	APPLE JUICE	5 pt (2.85 l)
1	VANILLA POD	3
2 tbsp	ARROWROOT	10 tbsp
1 tbsp	LEMON JUICE	2½ tbsp
4 tbsp	SOYA OIL	10 tbsp

1 Mix the dry ingredients for the crumble mix and then mix in the oil and apple juice.

2 Core and slice apples and pears and place in an oven-proof dish. Sprinkle with blackberries and the apple juice.

3 Cover with crumble mix and bake for 30 minutes at 350°F (180°C, gas mark 4).

4 To make the sauce, mix soya flour into apple juice, add vanilla pod and boil. Dissolve arrowroot in 2 tbsp of water, add lemon juice and stir into soya flour mixture. Simmer for 3 minutes. Remove the vanilla pod.

5 Heat the oil in a separate pan. Transfer the sauce mixture to a bowl and whisk in the oil a drop at a time as though making mayonnaise. The sauce should be thick like double cream.

6 Serve pie portions with a topping of the sauce.

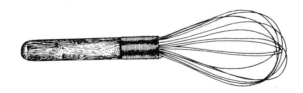

NUTRIENT ANALYSIS PER PORTION			
	kcal	kJ	MINERALS &
ENERGY (CALORIES)	360	1505	VITAMINS IN
	GRAMS (g)	AS % TOTAL ENERGY	LARGE AMOUNTS
TOTAL FAT	12.0	29.0	Potassium,
SATURATED FAT	1.7	4.2	iron, zinc
TOTAL CARBOHYDRATE	61.0	63.0	Vitamins
ADDED SUGARS	–	–	B₁, E
PROTEIN	7.0	7.8	
FIBRE	5.7g		
SALT	43.2mg		

ORANGES & KIWI FRUITS WITH MANDARIN NAPOLEON *(V, VG)*

Graham Scholey
Watford

10 portions		25 portions
10	ORANGES	25
2 oz (60 g)	SUGAR	10 oz (285 g)
10	KIWI FRUIT	25
1½ fl oz (40 ml)	ORANGE LIQUEUR	8 fl oz (250 ml)

1 Remove zest from oranges and cut into julienne strips. Blanch to soften.

2 Put sugar in thick-bottomed copper pan and just cover with water. Bring to boil, stirring, over strong heat but stop stirring when boils. Remove from heat when caramelised.

3 Let stand few minutes then add the orange julienne.

4 Peel pith from oranges and slice. Peel and slice kiwi fruit.

5 Place oranges and kiwi slices alternately in serving dish. Macerate with orange liqueur. When the caramelised zest liquor is cool, pour it over the fruit and serve.

NUTRIENT ANALYSIS PER PORTION			
	kcal	kJ	MINERALS & VITAMINS IN LARGE AMOUNTS
ENERGY (CALORIES)	120	502	
	GRAMS (g)	AS % TOTAL ENERGY	
TOTAL FAT	.57	4.20	Potassium
SATURATED FAT	–	–	Vitamin C
TOTAL CARBOHYDRATE	27.0	85.0	
ADDED SUGARS	7.0	22.0	
PROTEIN	1.8	5.9	
FIBRE	3.2g		
SALT	17.8mg		

FRUIT SALAD WITH MANGO & PASSION FRUIT SAUCE (V,VG)

Leith's Good Food
London

10 portions		25 portions
2	MANGOS	5
4	PASSION FRUIT	10
3 lb 2 oz (1.41 kg)	SEASONAL FRUITS LIKE GRAPES, RASPBERRIES, KIWIS, PEARS	8 lb (3.5 kg)
6 tbsp	COLD WATER	15 tbsp
10	MINT SPRIG	25
10	LIME SLICES	25

1 Process passion fruit pulp and mango flesh together with water for two minutes.

2 Prepare and slice chosen fruit.

3 Serve by pouring sauce onto individual flat pudding plates, arranging fruit on top and garnishing with sprig of mint and slice of lime.

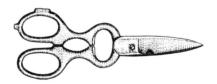

NUTRIENT ANALYSIS PER PORTION			
	kcal	kJ	MINERALS & VITAMINS IN LARGE AMOUNTS
ENERGY (CALORIES)	44	184	
	GRAMS (g)	AS % TOTAL ENERGY	
TOTAL FAT	–	–	Potassium
SATURATED FAT	–	–	Vitamin C
TOTAL CARBOHYDRATE	11.0	95.0	
ADDED SUGARS	–	–	
PROTEIN	.6	5.4	
FIBRE	2.6g		
SALT	18.1mg		

NECTARINE & RASPBERRY PANCAKES

Stuart Cabeldu Catering Ltd
London

10 portions		25 portions
5 oz (140 g)	WHOLEWHEAT FLOUR	12 oz (350 g)
2	SMALL EGGS	3
12 fl oz (350 ml)	SKIMMED MILK	1½ pt (850 ml)
1¼ oz (38 g)	SOLID POLYUNSATURATED VEGETABLE SHORTENING	3 oz (90 g)
6½ oz (185 g)	LOW-FAT CURD CHEESE	1 lb (450 g)
2½ tbsp	PLAIN LOW-FAT YOGHURT	6 tbsp
3	NECTARINES, SLICED AND DIPPED IN LEMON JUICE	6
6½ oz (185 g)	FRESH RASPBERRIES	1 lb (450 g)

1 Place flour in bowl, make well and add eggs. Stir in half the milk, beat thoroughly with wooden spoon and add remainder of milk.

2 Make pancakes and keep warm.

3 Combine curd cheese and yoghurt in food processor.

4 Place on one half of each pancake some curd cheese. Top with nectarine slices and raspberries then fold other half on top.

NUTRIENT ANALYSIS PER PORTION			
	kcal	kJ	MINERALS & VITAMINS IN LARGE AMOUNTS
ENERGY (CALORIES)	147	614	
	GRAMS (g)	AS % TOTAL ENERGY	
TOTAL FAT	6.7	41.0	None
SATURATED FAT	1.6	10.0	
TOTAL CARBOHYDRATE	14.0	35.0	
ADDED SUGARS	–	–	
PROTEIN	8.8	24.0	
FIBRE	3.0g		
SALT	.35g		

HEALTHY ORANGE CHEESECAKE *(V)*

Shirlee Posner
London

10 portions		25 portions
2	ORANGES	6
12 oz (350 g)	ROLLED OATS	1 lb 14 oz (860 g)
6 tbsp	HONEY	15 tbsp
1¹/₂ oz (45 g)	FLAKED ALMONDS	4 oz (115 g)
12 oz (350 g)	GREEK YOGHURT	2 lb 4 oz (1 kg)
8 oz (225 g)	FIRM, NATURAL TOFU OR COTTAGE CHEESE	1 lb 4 oz (550 g)

1 Remove zest from oranges and add it to oats, three-quarters of the honey, and the almonds. Mix and press into a flan tin. Chill.

2 Mix yoghurt, tofu and remaining honey in food processor. Pour into flan tin. Peel orange and thinly slice for decoration. Chill.

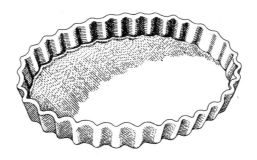

NUTRIENT ANALYSIS PER PORTION			
	kcal	kJ	MINERALS &
ENERGY (CALORIES)	284	1187	VITAMINS IN
	GRAMS (g)	AS % TOTAL ENERGY	LARGE AMOUNTS
TOTAL FAT	9.9	31.0	Potassium,
SATURATED FAT	3.9	9.8	calcium,
TOTAL CARBOHYDRATE	42.0	56.0	iron, zinc
ADDED SUGARS	13.0	17.0	Vitamin C
PROTEIN	9.1	13.0	
FIBRE	3.6g		
SALT	78.7mg		

ORANGE CHEESECAKE

Compass
London

10 portions		25 portions
10	DIGESTIVE BISCUITS, CRUSHED	25
2 oz (60 g)	POLYUNSATURATED MARGARINE, MELTED	2 lb 8 oz (1.1 kg)
1 lb (450 g)	COTTAGE CHEESE, SIEVED	2 lb 8 oz (1.1 kg)
2	EGGS	6
1 tbsp	CASTER SUGAR	3 tbsp
2½ tbsp	SELF-RAISING FLOUR	6 tbsp
5 fl oz (150 ml)	ORANGE JUICE	12½ fl oz (355 ml)
1½ tsp	GRATED ORANGE ZEST	5 tsp
4 oz (115 g)	SULTANAS	10 oz (285g)
	ORANGE SLICES FOR DECORATION	

1 Mix crushed biscuits and margarine, press firmly into flan tin.

2 Beat together cheese, eggs, sugar and flour. Gradually beat in orange juice and zest to a smooth mixture. Stir in sultanas. Pour over crumb base.

3 Bake at 325°F (160°C, gas mark 3) for 1 hour. Cool before serving. Decorate with sliced oranges.

NUTRIENT ANALYSIS PER PORTION			
	kcal	kJ	MINERALS & VITAMINS IN LARGE AMOUNTS
ENERGY (CALORIES)	227	949	
	GRAMS (g)	AS % TOTAL ENERGY	
TOTAL FAT	11.0	44.0	None
SATURATED FAT	3.5	14.0	
TOTAL CARBOHYDRATE	24.0	39.0	
ADDED SUGARS	4.3	7.0	
PROTEIN	9.9	17.0	
FIBRE	1.7g		
SALT	.89g		

OATY FRUIT CRUMBLE *(V)*

Miss H. B. Yeulett
Sussex

10 portions		25 portions
2½ lb (1.13 kg)	FRUIT (GOOSEBERRIES, PLUMS, PEARS, APPLES, BLACKBERRIES, BLACKCURRANTS, STRAWBERRIES)	6.25 lb (2.8 kg)
5 oz (140 g)	ROLLED OATS	12½ oz (365 g)
5 oz (140 g)	WHOLEMEAL FLOUR	12½ oz (365 g)
5 oz (140 g)	POLYUNSATURATED VEGETABLE MARGARINE	12½ oz (365 g)
2½ oz (75 g)	WHITE SUGAR	6¼ oz (180 g)

1 Wash and core fruit as necessary. Lightly stew in a little water.

2 Place fruit in oven-proof dish. Top with crumble mixture made by rubbing fat into flour and adding oats and sugar.

3 Bake at 375°F (190°C, gas mark 5) for 35 minutes or until brown on top.

NUTRIENT ANALYSIS PER PORTION			
	kcal	kJ	MINERALS & VITAMINS IN LARGE AMOUNTS
ENERGY (CALORIES)	269	1124	
	GRAMS (g)	AS % TOTAL ENERGY	
TOTAL FAT	13.0	43.0	Vitamin C
SATURATED FAT	2.27	7.6	
TOTAL CARBOHYDRATE	36.0	51.0	
ADDED SUGARS	7.9	11.0	
PROTEIN	4.10	6.0	
FIBRE	4.70g		
SALT	.3g		

APPLE & APRICOT CRUMBLE *(V,VG)*

Shirlee Posner
London

10 portions		25 portions
1 lb (450 g)	DRIED APRICOTS	2½ lb (1.1 kg)
1 pt (570 ml)	WATER	2½ pt (1.5 l)
¼ pt (150 ml)	APPLE JUICE	¾ pt (450 ml)
1 lb (450 g)	TINNED APPLES IN JUICE/FRESH APPLES, CORED AND SLICED	2½ lb (1.1 kg)
8 oz (225 g)	85% SR FLOUR	1½ lb (675 g)
4 oz (115 g)	DESICCATED COCONUT	12 oz (350 g)
4 oz (115 g)	POLYUNSATURATED PURE VEGETABLE MARGARINE	12 oz (350 g)

1 Soak apricots overnight in the water. Stew in their liquid with the apple juice and apples added.

2 Make a crumble with the flour, coconut and margarine.

3 Place apricot and apple mixture in oven-proof dish and top with crumble.
Bake at 350°F (180°C, gas mark 4) for 1 hour. Serve with yoghurt or Cashew Nut cream (p. 203).

NUTRIENT ANALYSIS PER PORTION			
	kcal	kJ	MINERALS & VITAMINS IN LARGE AMOUNTS
ENERGY (CALORIES)	334	1396	
	GRAMS (g)	AS % TOTAL ENERGY	
TOTAL FAT	17.0	45.0	Potassium,
SATURATED FAT	7.8	21.0	calcium,
TOTAL CARBOHYDRATE	44.0	49.0	iron
ADDED SUGARS	–	–	Vitamins
PROTEIN	5.1	6.1	A, E
FIBRE	15.0g		
SALT	.51g		

Opposite: *Poached Mignottes of Beef p. 150, Poached Pears in Blackcurrant Sauce p. 183.*

Over Page: *Venison with Plums p. 153, Bread and Butter Pudding p. 196.*

APPLE & GINGER CRUNCH
(V)

Compass
London

10 portions		25 portions
8 oz (225 g)	WHOLEMEAL FLOUR	1 lb 4 oz (565 g)
3 oz (90 g)	MEDIUM OATMEAL	8 oz (225 g)
2 tsp	GROUND GINGER	4 tsp
5 oz (140 g)	POLYUNSATURATED VEGETABLE MARGARINE	12 oz (350 g)
3 oz (90 g)	DEMERARA SUGAR	8 oz (225 g)
5 oz (140 g)	PORRIDGE OATS	12 oz (350 g)
2 lb 8 oz (1.1 kg)	COOKING APPLES, PEELED, CORED, THINLY SLICED	6 lb 4 oz (2.8 kg)
10 oz (225 g)	DRIED APRICOTS, COOKED, DRAINED AND CHOPPED	1 lb 8 oz (675 g)
6 fl oz (175 ml)	PURE ORANGE JUICE	15 fl oz (450 ml)

1 Make topping by mixing flour, oatmeal and ginger and then rubbing in the margarine.

2 Stir in the sugar and oats.

3 Arrange fruit in baking dish. Pour over orange juice and sprinkle topping mixture on top. Bake at 375°F (190°C, gas mark 5) for 25 minutes or until top browns.

NUTRIENT ANALYSIS PER PORTION			
ENERGY (CALORIES)	kcal 398	kJ 1664	MINERALS & VITAMINS IN LARGE AMOUNTS
	GRAMS (g)	AS % TOTAL ENERGY	
TOTAL FAT	14.0	31.0	Potassium,
SATURATED FAT	2.5	5.6	iron, zinc
TOTAL CARBOHYDRATE	65.0	61.0	Vitamins
ADDED SUGARS	8.4	7.9	B$_1$, C, E
PROTEIN	7.7	7.7	
FIBRE	13.0g		
SALT	.35g		

Previous Page: *Smoked Chicken Salad p. 145, Home-made Chinese Pancake Rolls p. 145.*

Opposite: *Fruit Salad with Mango and Passion Fruit Sauce p. 187, Orange Cheesecake p. 190, Apple and Ginger Crunch p. 193.*

FRUIT CRUMBLE (APPLE, RHUBARB OR GOOSEBERRY)

Aberdeen Royal Infirmary
Aberdeen

10 portions		25 portions
3.5 lb (1.5 kg)	CANNED SOLID PACK FRUIT	8 lb 12 oz (3.85 kg)
1½ oz (45 g)	FRUCTOSE	3 oz (90 g)
1½ oz (45 g)	WHOLEMEAL FLOUR	3 oz (90 g)
1½ oz (45 g)	WHITE FLOUR	3 oz (90 g)
1½ oz (45 g)	MARGARINE	3 oz (90 g)

1 Poach fruit until soft. Cool and add fructose (or non-calorie sweetener). Place in baking tin.

2 Make crumble by rubbing fat into flour until it resembles fine bread crumbs. Sprinkle on fruit.

3 Bake at 375°F (190°C, gas mark 5) for 40 minutes or until golden brown on top.

NUTRIENT ANALYSIS PER PORTION			
	kcal	kJ	MINERALS & VITAMINS IN LARGE AMOUNTS
ENERGY (CALORIES)	120	502	
	GRAMS (g)	AS % TOTAL ENERGY	
TOTAL FAT	5.7	43.0	Potassium,
SATURATED FAT	1.9	8.2	calcium
TOTAL CARBOHYDRATE	15.0	48.0	Vitamins
ADDED SUGARS	1.8	5.6	C, E
PROTEIN	2.7	8.9	
FIBRE	4.7g		
SALT	.2g		

OAT CRUMBLE *(V)*

Mary Deans
Edinburgh

10 portions		25 portions
½ lb (225 g)	CHOPPED DATES	*1¼ lb (565 g)*
½ pt (300 ml)	UNSWEETENED FRUIT JUICE	*1¼ pt (700 ml)*
2 lb (900 g)	COOKING APPLES	*5 lb (2.3 kg)*
4 oz (115 g)	POLYUNSATURATED VEGETABLE MARGARINE	*10 oz (285 g)*
6 oz (170 g)	WHOLEMEAL FLOUR	*1 lb (450 g)*
6 oz (170 g)	ROLLED OATS	*1 lb (450 g)*
2 oz (60 g)	DEMERARA SUGAR	*5 oz (140 g)*
2 oz (60 g)	SOYA OIL	*5 oz (140 g)*

1 Place dates and juice in pan, bring to boil.

2 Core and slice apples and arrange in oven-proof dish. Pour date mixture evenly over apples.

3 Rub margarine into flour until it resembles fine breadcrumbs. Add oats, sugar and oil. Mix well.

4 Sprinkle topping over fruit and bake at 350°F (180°C, gas mark 4) for 30–45 minutes or until brown on top.

5 Serve with low-fat yoghurt or semi-skimmed milk custard.

Other fruits may be substituted for apples, e.g. rhubarb and ginger, or pears and oranges.

NUTRIENT ANALYSIS PER PORTION			
	kcal	kJ	MINERALS &
ENERGY (CALORIES)	445	1860	VITAMINS IN
	GRAMS (g)	AS % TOTAL ENERGY	LARGE AMOUNTS
TOTAL FAT	17.0	35.0	Potassium,
SATURATED FAT	2.87	5.8	iron, zinc
TOTAL CARBOHYDRATE	71.0	60.0	Vitamin C
ADDED SUGARS	6.0	5.1	
PROTEIN	5.6	5.0	
FIBRE	8.9g		
SALT	.26g		

BREAD & BUTTER PUDDING

Compass
London

10 portions		25 portions
25	WHOLEMEAL BREAD SLICES	62
	POLYUNSATURATED MARGARINE FOR SPREADING	
8 oz (225 g)	MIXED DRIED FRUIT	1 lb 8 oz (675 g)
5	EGGS	13
1 pt 15 fl oz (1 l)	WATER	4 pt 10 fl oz (2.55 l)
4 oz (115 g)	SKIMMED MILK POWDER	10 oz (285 g)
	MIXED SPICE	

1 Remove crusts and spread bread with margarine. Cut into triangles or halves. Place layer of bread, margarine-side down in oven-proof dish and sprinkle with half the dried fruit. Add pinch spice.

2 Add another layer bread. margarine-side up, sprinkle with rest of fruit and add some spice. Add another layer of bread, margarine-side up.

3 Whisk eggs into milk and pour over bread. Leave ½ hour.

4 Sprinkle with spice then bake at 375°F (190°C, gas mark 5). Serve hot.

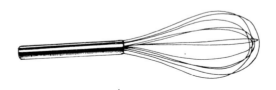

NUTRIENT ANALYSIS PER PORTION			
	kcal	kJ	MINERALS & VITAMINS IN LARGE AMOUNTS
ENERGY (CALORIES)	233	974	
	GRAMS (g)	AS % TOTAL ENERGY	
TOTAL FAT	5.4	21.0	Potassium,
SATURATED FAT	1.5	5.9	iron, zinc
TOTAL CARBOHYDRATE	37.0	60.0	Vitamins
ADDED SUGARS	–	–	B_2, B_{12}
PROTEIN	11.0	19.0	
FIBRE	4.9g		
SALT	.86g		

RICE PUDDING WITH FRUIT (V)

Mary Deans
Edinburgh

10 portions		25 portions
4 oz (115 g)	BROWN RICE, SHORT GRAIN	10 oz (285 g)
2 pt (1.1 l)	SEMI-SKIMMED MILK	5 pt (2.85 l)
4 oz (115 g)	SOFT BROWN SUGAR	10 oz (285 g)
2	EGGS, BEATEN	5
1 tsp	GROUND CINNAMON	2½ tsp
1 tsp	GRATED NUTMEG	2½ tsp
10 oz (285 g)	PITTED PRUNES, SOAKED AND DRAINED	1½ lb (675 g)
10 oz (285 g)	CANNED APRICOTS IN JUICE	1½ lb (675 g)
½ pt (300 ml)	LOW-FAT YOGHURT	1¼ pt (700 ml)

1 Boil milk and sprinkle in the rice. Cover and simmer 1 hour.
2 Remove from heat, mix in sugar, egg and spices.
3 Place half rice mixture in oven-proof dish. Drain apricots and mix with prunes. Make a layer of half the fruit on the rice. Add remaining rice and top with a layer of fruit.
4 Bake covered for ½ to ¾ hour at 350°F (180°C, gas mark 4).
5 Top with yoghurt and serve hot or cold.

NUTRIENT ANALYSIS PER PORTION			
	kcal	kJ	MINERALS &
ENERGY (CALORIES)	249	1041	VITAMINS IN
	GRAMS	AS % TOTAL	LARGE
	(g)	ENERGY	AMOUNTS
TOTAL FAT	3.9	14.0	Potassium,
SATURATED FAT	2.0	7.2	calcium,
TOTAL CARBOHYDRATE	48.0	73.0	Vitamin B$_2$
ADDED SUGARS	15.0	23.0	
PROTEIN	8.2	13.0	
FIBRE	5.5g		
SALT	.25g		

APRICOT MOUSSE *(V,VG)*

Jean-Claude Juston
London

10 portions		25 portions
2½ pt (1.5 l)	SOYA MILK	7 pt (3.95 l)
1 lb (450 g)	DRIED APRICOTS	2½ lb (1.1 kg)
	FRESH GRAPES FOR DECORATION	
	CINNAMON	

1 Soak apricots in soya milk overnight.
2 Blend apricots in liquid. Pour into serving bowls, top with a grape. Chill before serving. An optional addition is a pinch of cinnamon over the surface before serving.

NUTRIENT ANALYSIS PER PORTION			
	kcal	kJ	MINERALS & VITAMINS IN LARGE AMOUNTS
ENERGY (CALORIES)	151	631	
	GRAMS (g)	AS % TOTAL ENERGY	
TOTAL FAT	2.8	16.0	Potassium,
SATURATED FAT	.4	2.6	iron
TOTAL CARBOHYDRATE	30.0	74.0	Vitamin A
ADDED SUGARS	–	–	
PROTEIN	3.5	9.3	
FIBRE	11.0g		
SALT	88.9mg		

MANDARIN YOGHURT SNOW *(V)*

Rhonda Roberts
Auchenblae, Scotland

10 portions		25 portions
10½ oz (300 g)	TINNED MANDARINS IN NATURAL JUICE	1 lb 10½ oz (750 g)
¾ oz (20 g)	ARROWROOT	1½ oz (45 g)
5	EGG WHITES	12
5	SMALL CARTONS LOW-FAT NATURAL YOGHURT	12

1 Drain fruit and reserve juice. Arrange segments in one layer in a flan dish. Reserve some segments for decoration.

2 Dissolve the arrowroot in 3 fl oz (75 ml) of the juice and bring it gently to the boil. Remove from heat and leave to cool.

3 Whisk egg whites until stiff and then carefully fold in the yoghurt, followed by the cooled, thickened juice. Spread over mandarins. Decorate with reserved segments. Serve chilled.

NUTRIENT ANALYSIS PER PORTION			
ENERGY (CALORIES)	kcal 35	kJ 146	MINERALS & VITAMINS IN LARGE AMOUNTS
	GRAMS (g)	AS % TOTAL ENERGY	
TOTAL FAT	.1	1.3	Vitamin C
SATURATED FAT	.03	.8	
TOTAL CARBOHYDRATE	5.0	54.0	
ADDED SUGARS	–	–	
PROTEIN	3.9	45.0	
FIBRE	.15g		
SALT	.19g		

RHUBARB FOOL *(V)*

Leith's Good Food
London

10 portions		25 portions
2 lb 8 oz (1.1 kg)	RHUBARB	8 lb (3.5 kg)
2½	ORANGES, JUICE AND RINDS	5
10 oz (285 g)	FROMAGE BLANC	1 lb 8 oz (675 g)

1 Cut rhubarb into small pieces and stew gently in orange juice with rind added. (Add water if necessary to ensure rhubarb is just covered.)

2 Drain liquid and liquidise rhubarb. Tip into basin and whisk in fromage blanc. Serve chilled.

NUTRIENT ANALYSIS PER PORTION			
ENERGY (CALORIES)	kcal 38	kJ 159	MINERALS & VITAMINS IN LARGE AMOUNTS
	GRAMS (g)	AS % TOTAL ENERGY	
TOTAL FAT	.1	2.7	Potassium,
SATURATED FAT	.1	1.6	calcium
TOTAL CARBOHYDRATE	4.7	47.0	Vitamin C
ADDED SUGARS	–	–	
PROTEIN	4.8	51.0	
FIBRE	3.6g		
SALT	.33g		

BLACKCURRANT &
YOGHURT ICE *(V)*

Leith's Good Food
London

10 portions		25 portions
10 oz (285 g)	BLACKCURRANTS	1 lb 11 oz (770 g)
2 pt 10 fl oz (1.4 l)	LOW-FAT YOGHURT	6 pt 5 fl oz (3.8 l)
	LIQUID ARTIFICIAL SWEETENER	

1 Wash fruit, barely cover with water and stew gently for 20 minutes. Drain.

2 Mix fruit with yoghurt, sweeten to taste and pour into serving dish. Freeze until icy and half frozen. Tip into chilled bowl, whisk well and refreeze until almost solid.

3 Tip again into chilled bowl, whisk until smooth and freeze again. Remove from freezer 20 minutes before serving.

NUTRIENT ANALYSIS PER PORTION			
	kcal	kJ	MINERALS &
ENERGY (CALORIES)	81	339	VITAMINS IN
	GRAMS (g)	AS % TOTAL ENERGY	LARGE AMOUNTS
TOTAL FAT	1.4	16.0	Potassium,
SATURATED FAT	.8	9.2	calcium
TOTAL CARBOHYDRATE	11.0	49.0	Vitamins
ADDED SUGARS	–	–	B$_2$, C
PROTEIN	7.3	36.0	
FIBRE	2.5g		
SALT	.27g		

PINEAPPLE YOGHURT ICE CREAM *(V)*

Miss H. B. Yeulett
Sussex

10 portions		25 portions
2 lb (900 g)	TINNED PINEAPPLE IN NATURAL JUICE	5 lb (2.3 kg)
2½ tbsp	HONEY	2½ tbsp
2½ tbsp	LEMON JUICE	2½ tbsp
25 oz (705 g)	LOW-FAT NATURAL YOGHURT	3 lb 14 oz (1.7 l)

1 Drain pineapple juice into pan. Add honey and lemon juice and heat until dissolved. Leave to cool and stir in yoghurt.

2 Pour into shallow container and freeze.

3 Remove from freezer and stir in the crushed pineapple. Return to freezer until solid. Transfer to refrigerator 1 hour before serving.

NUTRIENT ANALYSIS PER PORTION			
ENERGY (CALORIES)	kcal 128	kJ 535	MINERALS & VITAMINS IN LARGE AMOUNTS
	GRAMS (g)	AS % TOTAL ENERGY	
TOTAL FAT	.71	5.0	Calcium
SATURATED FAT	.41	2.9	Vitamin C
TOTAL CARBOHYDRATE	28.0	83.0	
ADDED SUGARS	14.0	42.0	
PROTEIN	3.8	12.0	
FIBRE	.81g		
SALT	.14g		

APRICOT & ORANGE MOUSSE

Miss H. B. Yeulett
Sussex

10 portions		25 portions
20 oz (570 g)	DRIED APRICOTS	50 oz (1.41 kg)
1¼ oz (40 g)	GELATIN, POWDERED	3¼ oz (100 g)
3 tbsp	ORANGE JUICE, UNSWEETENED	8 tbsp
7	EGG WHITES	18

1 Soak apricots overnight in 2 pints (1.1 l) water. Bring to boil and simmer for 1 hour or until very soft.

2 Dissolve gelatin in 6 tbsp water over gentle heat.

3 Blend apricots. Add orange juice and gelatin.

4 Whisk egg whites until stiff and fold into apricots. Place in individual dishes and leave in refrigerator to set. Decorate with twists of orange.

NUTRIENT ANALYSIS PER PORTION			
	kcal	kJ	MINERALS & VITAMINS IN LARGE AMOUNTS
ENERGY (CALORIES)	130	543	
	GRAMS (g)	AS % TOTAL ENERGY	
TOTAL FAT	–	–	Potassium,
SATURATED FAT	–	–	iron
TOTAL CARBOHYDRATE	24.0	71.0	Vitamin A
ADDED SUGARS	–	–	
PROTEIN	9.5	29.0	
FIBRE	13g		
SALT	.27g		

CASHEW NUT CREAM
(V , VG)

Shirlee Posner
London

10 portions		25 portions
8 oz (225 g)	CASHEW NUTS OR PIECES	1 lb 4 oz (565 g)
10 oz (285 g)	WATER	25 oz (705 g)
1 tbsp	CLEAR HONEY	2¹/₂ tbsp
1 tsp	VANILLA ESSENCE	2¹/₂ tsp

1 Blend all ingredients until smooth.

This is a delicious cream in its own right and is an ideal substitute for dairy cream. It goes very well with fruit crumbles, pies, tarts, etc.

NUTRIENT ANALYSIS PER PORTION			
	kcal	kJ	MINERALS & VITAMINS IN LARGE AMOUNTS
ENERGY (CALORIES)	137	573	
	GRAMS (g)	AS % TOTAL ENERGY	
TOTAL FAT	11.0	73.0	None
SATURATED FAT	1.17	7.70	
TOTAL CARBOHYDRATE	5.6	15.0	
ADDED SUGARS	1.9	5.2	
PROTEIN	4.1	12.0	
FIBRE	.2g		
SALT	12.5mg		

APPENDIX I
VITAMINS AND MINERALS

The table shows the main minerals and vitamins needed for health:

Mineral	Function	Food source
Calcium	Vital for healthy bones & teeth; also important in the blood and for healthy heart muscles and nerves	The skim part of milk, yogurt, cheese, sardines, watercress, bread, hard tap water
Iron	Found in the red colour of blood and muscle protein	Meat, liver, eggs, white bread flour, figs, dried apricots, cocoa
Magnesium	Important for good bones and enzymes	Nearly all food, especially all green vegetables, bread, milk, eggs, meat, peanuts
Phosphorus	Found in bone, all cells and necessary for many regular functions of the body	Nearly all foods, vegetables, meat, milk, bread
Potassium	Found in all cells and has a role in the fluid balances	Most foods but vegetables, fruit and meat are good sources
Sodium & Chloride	Maintain the water and fluid balance of the body	Small amounts in nearly all foods

Trace elements (needed in very small amounts)

Chromium	Metabolism of fat and sugar	Cereals, fruits
Cobalt	Necessary for Vitamin B_{12}	Vitamin B_{12} in meats and yeast extract
Copper	Necessary for some enzymes to function	Most foods
Fluorine	For strong teeth and bones	Water, tea, fish bones
Iodine	Found in the hormone Thyroxine	Fish, fruit and vegetables
Manganese	Necessary in enzymes	Cereals and nuts, tea
Selenium	Necessary for Vitamin E	Most foods
Zinc	Important for enzymes to function	Most foods

Vitamin	Function	Food source
Vitamin A	Seeing in dim light and healthy skin	Liver, cheese, eggs, green leafy vegetables, carrots, dried apricots, tomatoes
Thiamin (B_1)	Metabolism of carbohydrate	Skim of milk, pork, peas, cereals, potatoes
Riboflavin (B_2)	Utilisation of energy from food	Skim of milk, cheese, liver, meat, eggs
Nicotinic acid	Utilisation of energy from food	Skim of milk, cheese, eggs, meat, peas, white flour
Vitamin B_6	Metabolism of amino acids (in proteins)	Meat, eggs, fish, cereals, green vegetables
Vitamin B_{12}	Essential for cells to divide in growth and blood formation	Liver, meat, eggs, yeast extract
Folic acid	Works with B_{12} and other functions in healthy blood	Offal meats and green vegetables, peas and beans, bread, bananas

Vitamin	Function	Food source
Pantothenic acid	Release of energy from fat	In most meats, cereals and vegetables
Biotin	Metabolism of fat	Offal, egg yolks
Vitamin C	Essential for connective tissue	Green vegetables, potatoes, blackcurrants, citrus fruit, tomatoes
Vitamin D	Important for movement and holding of calcium	Eggs, oily fish, margarine, Ovaltine
Vitamin E	Not clear, but can get anaemia if deficient	Vegetable oil, cereals, eggs
Vitamin K	Necessary for blood clotting	Most vegetables and cereals

Source: Robbins, C. J., *Eating for Health*, London, Granada, 1985.

APPENDIX II
FAT ANALYSIS OF SOME COMMON MARGARINES, FATS AND OILS

FOOD	g fat in food	% saturated fat in fat	% polyunsaturated fat in fat
Blue band margarine	75	22	34
Flora	81	23	52.7
Krona	72	43	6.7
Safeway 100% Soya	75	15.3	64.3
Sainsbury's Soya	77	19.4	45.3
Stork SB	72	26	18
Stork hard	66	38.3	8.5
White Flora	84	18.2	45.8
Coconut oil	100	90	1.7
Corn (maize) oil	100	16.4	50.5
Cottonseed oil	100	25.6	48.1
Olive oil	100	14	11.2
Palm oil	100	45	8.3
Peanut oil	100	19	28.8
Rapeseed oil	100	6.6	32
Safflower oil	100	10.2	72.5
Soyabean oil	100	14	57
Sunflowerseed oil	100	13	50.3
Crisp and Dry oil	95	12.9	52
Lard	99	39.8	11.4
Shredded suet	80	61.2	2.5
Beef fat (cooked)	59	45	4.3
Lamb fat (cooked)	58	53	5.2
Pork fat (cooked)	57	43	8.4
Butter	77	58	1.5

Source: Data supplied by Professor Crawford, Nuffield Institute of Comparative Medicine Laboratories, London.

APPENDIX III
RECOMMENDED DAILY AMOUNTS OF NUTRIENTS
FOR POPULATION GROUPS
(DEPARTMENT OF HEALTH AND SOCIAL SECURITY, 1979)

Age ranges years		Energy		Protein	Calcium	Iron	Vitamin A (retinol equivalent)
		MJ	kcal	g	mg	mg	μg
Boys							
Under 1		3.25	780	19	600	6	450
1		5.0	1,200	30	600	7	300
2		5.75	1,400	35	600	7	300
3–4		6.5	1,560	39	600	8	300
5–6		7.25	1,740	43	600	10	300
7–8		8.25	1,980	49	600	10	400
9–11		9.5	2,280	56	700	12	575
12–14		11.0	2,640	66	700	12	725
15–17		12.0	2,880	72	600	12	750
Girls							
Under 1		3.0	720	18	600	6	450
1		4.5	1,100	27	600	7	300
2		5.5	1,300	32	600	7	300
3–4		6.25	1,500	37	600	8	300
5–6		7.0	1,680	42	600	10	300
7–8		8.0	1,900	48	600	10	400
9–11		8.5	2,050	51	700	12[2]	575
12–14		9.0	2,150	53	700	12[2]	725
15–17		9.0	2,150	53	600	12[2]	750
Men							
	Sedentary	10.5	2,510	62	500	10	750
18–34	Moderately active	12.0	2,900	72	500	10	750
	Very active	14.0	3,350	84	500	10	750
	Sedentary	10.0	2,400	60	500	10	750
35–64	Moderately active	11.5	2,750	69	500	10	750
	Very active	14.0	3,350	84	500	10	750
65–74		10.0	2,400	60	500	10	750
75 and over		9.0	2,150	54	500	10	750
Women							
18–54	Most occupations	9.0	2,150	54	500	12[2]	750
	Very active	10.5	2,500	62	500	12[2]	750
55–74		8.0	1,900	47	500	10	750
75 and over		7.0	1,680	42	500	10	750
Pregnant		10.0	2,400	60	1,200	13	750
Lactating		11.5	2,750	69	1,200	15	1,200

[1] Most people who go out in the sun need no dietary source of vitamin D, but children and adolescents in winter, and housebound adults, are recommended to take 10μg vitamin D daily.

Thiamin	Riboflavin	Nicotinic acid equivalent	Total folic acid	Vitamin C	Vitamin D[1]
mg	mg	mg	μg	mg	μg
0.3	0.4	5	50	·20	7.5
0.5	0.6	7	100	20	10
0.6	0.7	8	100	20	10
0.6	0.8	9	100	20	10
0.7	0.9	10	200	20	—
0.8	1.0	11	200	20	—
0.9	1.2	14	200	25	—
1.1	1.4	16	300	25	—
1.2	1.7	19	300	30	—
0.3	0.4	5	50	20	7.5
0.4	0.6	7	100	20	10
0.5	0.7	8	100	20	10
0.6	0.8	9	100	20	10
0.7	0.9	10	200	20	—
0.8	1.0	11	200	20	—
0.8	1.2	14	300	25	—
0.9	1.4	16	300	25	—
0.9	1.7	19	300	30	—
1.0	1.6	18	300	30	—
1.2	1.6	18	300	30	—
1.3	1.6	18	300	30	—
1.0	1.6	18	300	30	—
1.1	1.6	18	300	30	—
1.3	1.6	18	300	30	—
1.0	1.6	18	300	30	—
0.9	1.6	18	300	30	—
0.9	1.3	15	300	30	—
1.0	1.3	15	300	30	—
0.8	1.3	15	300	30	—
0.7	1.3	15	300	30	—
1.0	1.6	18	500	60	10
1.1	1.8	21	400	60	10

[2] These iron recommendations may not cover heavy menstrual losses.

APPENDIX IV

CONTRIBUTIONS MADE BY GROUPS OF FOODS TO THE NUTRITIONAL VALUE OF HOUSEHOLD FOOD: NATIONAL AVERAGES, 1986

(PER PERSON PER DAY)

	Energy			Protein		Fat		Fatty acids						Carbo-hydrate		Calcium		Iron	
								Saturated		Mono-unsaturated		Poly-unsaturated							
	kcal	MJ	Per cent of total	g	Per cent of total	g	Per cent of total	g	Per cent of total	g	Per cent of total	g	Per cent of total	g	Per cent of total	mg	Per cent of total	mg	Per cent of total
Liquid wholemilk	167	0.70	8.1	8.2	11.9	10.1	10.3	6.4	15.7	2.8	7.7	0.3	2.2	12	4.8	291	32.6	0.1	1.2
Dried milk	3	0.01	0.1	0.1	0.1	0.1	0.1	0.1	0.2	—	0.1	—	0.1	—	0.1	2	0.3	—	0.3
Other milk and cream	41	0.20	2.0	3.2	4.6	1.7	1.8	1.0	2.4	0.5	1.3	0.1	0.9	6	2.3	102	11.4	0.1	0.7
Cheese	64	0.26	3.1	4.1	5.9	5.2	5.3	3.2	7.8	1.4	4.0	0.2	1.3	—		123	13.8	0.1	0.6
Total milk, cream and cheese	275	1.18	13.3	15.6	22.5	17.1	17.5	10.6	26.0	4.7	13.1	0.7	4.6	18	7.2	518	58.1	0.3	2.7
Beef and veal	57	0.24	2.8	4.7	6.8	4.3	4.4	1.7	4.3	2.0	5.7	0.2	1.1	—		2	0.2	0.5	4.6
Mutton and lamb	31	0.13	1.5	1.6	2.2	2.8	2.8	1.3	3.2	1.1	3.0	0.1	0.8	—		—	0.1	0.1	1.1
Pork	39	0.16	1.9	2.1	3.0	3.5	3.6	1.2	3.0	1.6	4.4	0.4	2.8	—		1	0.1	0.1	0.9
Bacon and ham, uncooked	38	0.16	1.9	2.0	2.9	3.4	3.4	1.3	3.2	1.5	4.2	0.4	2.5	—		1	0.1	0.1	0.9
Liver	3	0.01	0.2	0.5	0.7	0.1	0.1	—	0.1	—	0.1	—	0.2	—		—		0.2	1.8
Poultry, uncooked	31	0.13	1.5	3.2	4.7	2.0	2.0	0.6	1.6	0.9	2.5	0.4	2.7	—		1	0.1	0.1	1.0
Sausages	33	0.14	1.6	1.1	1.6	2.8	2.8	1.1	2.6	1.3	3.6	0.3	1.9	1	0.4	4	0.5	0.1	1.1
Other meat and meat products	94	0.39	4.5	5.2	7.5	6.4	6.5	2.6	6.4	2.8	7.8	0.5	3.7	4	1.7	13	1.4	0.8	6.7
Total meat	327	1.36	15.8	20.4	29.4	25.2	25.7	9.9	24.3	11.1	31.1	2.2	15.7	5	2.2	23	2.5	2.1	18.2
Fat fish	10	0.04	0.5	0.9	1.4	0.7	0.7	0.1	0.4	0.3	0.7	0.2	1.5	—		7	0.8	0.1	0.7
Other fish and fish products	20	0.08	1.0	2.5	3.5	0.7	0.7	0.2	0.4	0.2	0.7	0.2	1.6	1	0.4	8	0.9	0.1	1.2
Total fish	30	0.12	1.4	3.4	4.9	1.4	1.5	0.3	0.8	0.5	1.4	0.4	3.1	1	0.4	15	1.7	0.2	1.9
Eggs	34	0.14	1.7	2.7	3.9	2.6	2.7	0.7	1.8	1.2	3.2	0.3	1.9	—		12	1.4	0.4	3.9
Butter	68	0.28	3.3	—	0.1	7.5	7.6	4.9	11.9	1.9	5.5	0.3	1.9	—		1	0.2	—	0.1
Margarine	122	0.50	5.9	—		13.5	13.8	4.0	9.9	5.4	15.0	3.5	24.6	—		2	0.3	0.1	0.5
All other fats	124	0.51	6.0	0.3	0.4	13.4	13.7	4.3	10.5	5.5	15.4	3.0	20.8	—	0.2	—		—	0.1
Total fats	314	1.29	15.1	0.3	0.5	34.4	35.1	13.2	32.4	12.8	35.8	6.8	47.3	1	0.2	4	0.5	0.1	0.7

Potatoes	91	0.39	4.4	2.3	3.4	0.2	0.2	—	0.1	—	—	0.1	1.0	21	8.7	6	0.6	0.5	4.1
Cabbage, brussels sprouts and cauliflower	4	0.02	0.2	0.6	0.9	—	—	—	—	—	—	—	—	1	0.2	9	1.0	0.1	1.1
Leafy salads	—	—	—	—	0.1	—	—	—	—	—	—	—	—	—	—	1	0.1	—	0.4
Fresh legumes, including frozen	7	0.03	0.4	0.6	0.9	0.1	0.1	—	—	—	—	—	0.3	1	0.5	5	0.5	0.2	1.5
Other green vegetables	—	—	—	—	—	—	—	—	—	—	—	—	—	—	—	1	0.1	—	0.2
Fresh tomatoes	2	0.01	0.1	0.1	0.2	—	—	—	—	—	—	—	—	—	0.2	2	0.2	0.1	0.5
Carrots	3	0.01	0.1	0.1	0.1	—	—	—	—	—	—	—	—	1	0.3	6	0.7	0.1	0.6
Other root vegetables	2	0.01	0.1	0.1	0.1	—	—	—	—	—	—	—	—	—	0.2	3	0.3	—	0.2
Other vegetables and vegetable products	82	0.35	4.0	2.8	4.1	2.6	2.7	0.7	1.6	0.9	2.6	0.9	6.1	13	5.2	26	2.9	0.9	8.0
Total vegetables	191	0.81	9.3	6.8	9.8	2.8	2.9	0.7	1.7	0.9	2.6	1.0	7.3	37	15.2	58	6.5	1.9	16.7
Oranges	3	0.01	0.2	0.1	0.1	—	—	—	—	—	—	—	—	1	0.3	4	0.4	—	0.2
Other citrus fruit	1	0.01	0.1	—	—	—	—	—	—	—	—	—	—	—	0.1	2	0.2	—	0.2
Apples and pears	11	0.05	0.5	0.1	0.2	—	—	—	—	—	—	—	—	3	1.1	1	0.2	0.1	0.7
Soft fruit	2	0.01	0.1	—	0.1	—	—	—	—	—	—	—	—	1	0.2	1	0.2	—	0.3
Bananas	6	0.03	0.3	0.1	0.1	—	—	—	—	—	—	—	0.1	2	0.6	—	0.1	—	0.3
Other fresh fruit	2	0.01	0.1	—	0.1	—	0.1	—	—	—	0.1	—	—	—	0.2	2	0.2	—	0.3
Other fruit and fruit products	28	0.12	1.3	0.4	0.6	1.0	1.0	0.3	0.7	0.4	1.2	0.3	2.0	4	1.8	5	0.5	0.2	1.5
Fruit juices	15	0.06	0.7	0.1	0.1	—	—	—	—	—	—	—	—	4	1.6	3	0.3	0.1	0.6
Total fruit	68	0.29	3.3	0.9	1.4	1.1	1.1	0.3	0.7	0.4	1.2	0.3	2.1	15	6.0	18	2.0	0.5	4.1
White bread (standard loaves)	151	0.64	7.3	5.4	7.7	1.0	1.1	0.2	0.5	0.2	0.5	0.3	2.2	32	13.2	68	7.6	1.0	8.8
Other bread	134	0.57	6.5	5.3	7.7	1.4	1.5	0.3	0.8	0.3	0.8	0.4	2.9	27	10.9	52	5.9	1.4	12.7
Flour	56	0.24	2.7	1.5	2.2	0.2	0.2	—	0.1	—	0.1	0.1	0.7	13	5.3	41	4.6	0.3	3.0
Cakes and pastries	50	0.21	2.4	0.8	1.2	1.9	1.9	0.8	1.9	0.7	1.9	0.3	1.8	8	3.2	13	1.5	0.2	1.9
Biscuits	106	0.45	5.1	1.5	2.2	4.9	5.0	2.4	5.8	1.6	4.5	0.5	3.4	15	6.2	22	2.5	0.5	4.3
Breakfast cereals	62	0.26	3.0	1.8	2.5	0.4	0.4	0.1	0.2	0.1	0.3	0.2	1.2	14	5.6	7	0.8	1.3	11.5
Other cereals	68	0.29	3.3	1.5	2.1	1.5	1.5	0.5	1.3	0.5	1.4	0.3	1.9	13	5.3	15	1.7	0.3	2.9
Total cereals	626	2.66	30.3	17.8	25.7	11.4	11.6	4.3	10.5	3.5	9.7	2.0	14.0	121	49.7	218	24.5	5.1	45.0
Tea	—	—	—	—	—	—	—	—	—	—	—	—	—	—	—	2	0.3	0.1	0.6
Other beverages	7	0.03	0.3	0.5	0.7	0.1	0.1	0.1	0.1	—	0.1	—	—	1	0.5	5	0.5	0.2	1.4
Total beverages	7	0.03	0.3	0.5	0.7	0.1	0.1	0.1	0.1	—	0.1	—	—	1	0.5	7	0.8	0.3	2.0
Other foods	43	0.18	2.1	1.0	1.4	1.9	1.9	0.6	1.5	0.6	1.7	0.6	3.9	6	2.4	17	1.9	0.5	4.0
TOTAL ALL FOODS	2064	8.70	100	69.3	100	98.1	100	40.6	100	35.8	100	14.3	100	244	100	893	100	11.3	100

Contributions made by groups of foods to the nutritional value of household food (continued)

	Thiamin (a)		Riboflavin		Nicotinic acid		Tryptophan		Nicotinic acid equivalent		Vitamin C (a)		Vitamin A Retinol		Vitamin A Carotene		Vitamin A Retinol equivalent		Vitamin D	
	mg	Per cent of total	mg	Per cent of total	mg	Per cent of total	mg	Per cent of total	mg	Per cent of total	mg	Per cent of total	µg	Per cent of total	µg	Per cent of total	µg	Per cent of total	µg	Per cent of total
Liquid wholemilk	0.09	6.2	0.43	23.4	0.2	1.3	119.0	13.4	2.2	7.7	1.7	2.9	131.9	13.6	60	2.8	141	10.7	0.07	2.3
Dried milk	0.01	0.4	0.01	0.5	—	0.3	1.0	0.1	0.1	0.2	0.5	0.8	3.3	0.3	1	—	3	0.3	0.04	1.4
Other milk and cream	0.04	2.6	0.15	8.0	0.1	0.8	44.4	5.0	0.8	3.0	0.8	1.3	24.9	2.6	9	0.4	26	2.0	0.15	4.7
Cheese	0.01	0.5	0.08	4.2	—	0.1	58.2	6.6	1.0	3.5	—	—	52.1	5.4	22	1.0	56	4.2	0.04	1.3
Total milk, cream and cheese	0.13	9.7	0.66	36.1	0.3	2.6	222.5	25.1	4.0	14.4	3.0	5.0	212.2	21.9	92	4.3	227	17.1	0.31	9.6
Beef and veal	0.01	0.5	0.06	3.2	1.0	7.9	59.6	6.7	2.0	7.3	—	—	0.9	0.1	4	0.2	2	0.1	—	—
Mutton and lamb	0.01	0.4	0.02	1.0	0.4	3.2	19.7	2.2	0.7	2.7	—	—	—	—	—	—	—	—	—	—
Pork	0.05	3.5	0.02	1.2	0.5	4.2	23.2	2.6	0.9	3.3	—	—	—	—	—	—	—	—	—	—
Bacon and ham, uncooked	0.04	3.0	0.02	1.2	0.5	4.1	19.1	2.2	0.9	3.0	—	—	—	—	—	—	—	—	—	—
Liver	0.01	0.4	0.09	4.8	0.3	2.6	5.8	0.7	0.4	1.6	0.4	0.6	413.9	42.7	7	0.3	415	31.2	0.02	0.5
Poultry, uncooked	0.01	1.0	0.02	1.3	1.0	7.4	35.9	4.0	1.6	5.6	—	—	4.4	0.5	—	—	4	0.3	—	—
Sausages	—	0.2	0.01	0.7	0.3	2.4	14.6	1.6	0.6	2.0	—	—	—	—	—	—	—	—	—	—
Other meat and meat products	0.06	4.4	0.08	4.5	1.0	7.6	69.5	7.8	2.1	7.6	0.8	1.3	42.8	4.4	8	0.4	44	3.3	0.01	0.2
Total meat	0.19	13.6	0.33	17.9	5.1	39.4	247.5	27.9	9.2	33.0	1.1	1.9	462.1	47.7	19	0.9	466	35.1	0.03	0.8
Fat fish	—	0.2	0.01	0.6	0.3	2.5	10.1	1.1	0.5	1.8	—	0.1	1.7	0.2	—	—	2	0.1	0.48	14.7
Other fish and fish products	0.01	0.7	0.01	0.6	0.3	2.4	26.9	3.0	0.8	2.7	—	—	0.5	0.1	—	—	—	—	0.01	0.4
Total fish	0.01	0.9	0.02	1.3	0.6	4.9	37.0	4.2	1.3	4.5	—	0.1	2.1	0.2	—	—	2	0.2	0.49	15.1
Eggs	0.02	1.2	0.10	5.6	—	0.1	48.1	5.4	0.8	2.9	—	—	41.7	4.3	—	—	42	3.1	0.33	10.2
Butter	—	—	—	—	—	—	0.6	0.1	—	—	—	—	69.0	7.1	43	2.0	76	5.7	0.07	2.1
Margarine	—	—	—	—	—	—	—	—	—	—	—	—	132.3	13.6	49	2.3	141	10.6	1.32	40.7
All other fats	—	—	—	—	—	—	3.9	0.4	0.1	0.2	0.1	0.1	34.9	3.6	3	0.1	35	2.7	0.28	8.6
Total fats	—	—	—	—	—	—	4.5	0.5	0.1	0.3	—	0.1	236.2	24.4	95	4.4	252	19.0	1.67	51.5
Sugar and preserves	—	—	—	—	—	—	0.2	—	—	—	0.6	1.1	—	—	1	0.1	—	—	—	—
Potatoes	0.16	11.2	0.03	1.8	0.6	4.5	35.2	4.0	1.2	4.4	8.3	14.0	—	—	—	—	—	—	—	—
Cabbage, brussels sprouts and cauliflower	0.01	0.8	0.02	1.0	0.1	0.8	7.2	0.8	0.2	0.8	3.4	5.7	—	—	51	2.3	8	0.6	—	—

Table (continuation; column headings appear on the preceding page). Each of the ten data columns is given as *amount (per cent of total)*.

Food	(1)	(2)	(3)	(4)	(5)	(6)	(7)	(8)	(9)	(10)
Leafy salads	— (—)	— (0.3)	— (0.1)	0.5 (0.1)	— (0.1)	0.9 (1.5)	— (—)	52 (2.4)	9 (0.7)	— (—)
Fresh legumes, including frozen	0.02 (1.7)	0.01 (0.7)	0.2 (1.5)	5.5 (0.6)	0.3 (1.0)	1.3 (2.3)	— (—)	45 (2.1)	7 (0.6)	— (—)
Other fresh green vegetables	— (0.1)	— (0.1)	0.1 (0.8)	0.4 (0.1)	0.1 (0.4)	— (—)	— (—)	42 (1.9)	7 (0.5)	— (—)
Fresh tomatoes	0.01 (0.6)	0.01 (0.3)	0.1 (0.8)	0.9 (0.1)	0.1 (0.4)	2.9 (4.9)	— (—)	88 (4.1)	15 (1.1)	— (—)
Carrots	0.01 (0.4)	0.01 (0.3)	0.1 (0.5)	0.7 (0.1)	0.1 (0.3)	0.6 (0.9)	— (—)	1333 (61.8)	222 (16.7)	— (—)
Other root vegetables	— (0.2)	— (0.2)	0.1 (0.3)	0.8 (0.1)	0.1 (0.2)	0.6 (0.9)	— (—)	3 (0.1)	3 (0.1)	— (—)
Other vegetables and vegetable products	0.06 (4.5)	0.06 (3.0)	0.9 (6.6)	35.0 (3.9)	1.4 (5.0)	8.5 (14.3)	— (—)	186 (8.6)	31 (2.3)	— (—)
Total vegetables	0.27 (19.6)	0.14 (7.6)	2.0 (15.2)	86.1 (9.7)	3.4 (12.3)	26.5 (44.6)	— (—)	1799 (83.4)	299 (22.5)	— (—)
Oranges	0.01 (0.6)	— (0.2)	— (0.1)	0.4 (0.1)	0.1 (0.1)	4.2 (7.1)	— (—)	4 (0.2)	1 (0.1)	— (—)
Other citrus fruit	— (0.2)	— (0.1)	— (0.1)	0.2 (—)	0.1 (0.1)	1.9 (3.3)	— (—)	3 (0.1)	— (—)	— (—)
Apples and pears	0.01 (0.7)	0.01 (0.3)	— (0.2)	0.7 (0.1)	0.1 (0.1)	2.2 (3.7)	— (—)	8 (0.4)	1 (0.1)	— (—)
Soft fruit	— (0.1)	— (0.1)	— (0.1)	0.4 (—)	0.1 (0.1)	1.9 (3.1)	— (—)	3 (0.1)	— (—)	— (—)
Bananas	— (0.2)	0.01 (0.3)	0.2 (0.4)	1.0 (0.1)	0.2 (0.7)	0.8 (1.3)	— (—)	16 (0.7)	3 (0.2)	— (—)
Other fresh fruit	— (0.2)	— (0.1)	— (—)	0.2 (—)	0.1 (0.2)	0.7 (1.2)	— (—)	28 (1.3)	5 (0.4)	— (—)
Other fresh fruit and fruit products	0.01 (0.6)	0.01 (0.5)	0.2 (—)	4.9 (0.5)	0.3 (1.1)	0.8 (1.4)	— (—)	17 (0.8)	3 (0.2)	— (—)
Fruit juices	0.02 (1.3)	— (0.3)	0.2 (—)	1.9 (0.4)	0.1 (0.3)	14.3 (24.0)	— (—)	2 (0.1)	2 (0.1)	— (—)
Total fruit	0.05 (3.9)	0.03 (1.8)	0.4 (3.4)	9.7 (1.1)	2.1 (7.5)	26.8 (45.0)	— (—)	80 (3.7)	13 (1.0)	— (—)
White bread (standard loaves)	0.14 (9.9)	0.04 (2.0)	— (—)	66.9 (7.5)	1.5 (5.3)	— (—)	— (—)	— (—)	— (—)	— (—)
Other bread	0.19 (13.9)	0.08 (4.4)	— (—)	64.0 (7.2)	1.3 (4.5)	— (—)	— (—)	— (—)	— (—)	— (—)
Flour	0.05 (3.8)	0.01 (0.4)	— (—)	19.1 (2.2)	0.4 (1.6)	— (—)	— (—)	— (—)	— (—)	— (—)
Cakes and pastries	0.01 (1.0)	0.01 (0.7)	— (—)	10.7 (1.2)	0.2 (0.8)	— (—)	8.5 (0.9)	1 (—)	8 (0.6)	0.07 (2.1)
Biscuits	0.03 (2.5)	0.04 (2.0)	0.1 (0.7)	17.9 (2.0)	0.4 (1.4)	— (—)	— (0.1)	— (—)	— (—)	— (—)
Other cereals and cereal products	0.04 (2.7)	0.02 (1.2)	0.3 (—)	17.6 (2.0)	0.3 (1.2)	— (—)	3.2 (0.3)	5 (0.2)	4 (0.3)	0.05 (1.6)
Breakfast cereals	0.19 (13.9)	0.21 (11.4)	2.4 (18.0)	19.2 (2.2)	2.7 (9.6)	0.4 (0.7)	— (—)	— (—)	— (—)	0.27 (8.4)
Total cereals	0.66 (47.6)	0.40 (22.1)	3.3 (24.9)	215.3 (24.3)	6.8 (24.4)	0.6 (1.0)	11.7 (1.2)	6 (0.3)	13 (1.0)	0.39 (12.0)
Tea	0.01 (0.5)	0.07 (3.9)	0.1 (0.5)	— (—)	0.1 (0.5)	— (—)	— (—)	— (—)	1 (0.1)	— (—)
Other beverages	0.01 (0.6)	0.01 (0.8)	0.8 (—)	5.9 (0.7)	0.8 (2.8)	— (—)	1.3 (0.1)	1 (0.1)	1 (0.1)	— (0.7)
Total beverages	0.02 (1.1)	0.09 (4.7)	0.8 (—)	5.9 (0.7)	0.9 (3.3)	— (—)	1.3 (0.1)	1 (0.1)	1 (0.1)	— (0.7)
Other foods	0.03 (2.4)	0.05 (2.9)	0.8 (—)	11.2 (1.3)	0.8 (2.9)	0.8 (1.3)	2.5 (0.3)	65 (3.0)	13 (1.0)	— (0.2)
TOTAL ALL FOODS	1.39 (100)	1.82 (100)	13.1 (100)	887.9 (100)	28.0 (100)	59.5 (100)	969.8 (100)	2157 (100)	1328 (100)	3.2 (100)

(a) Cooking losses have been taken into account. Intake figures for thiamin allow for a loss of 50 per cent from beef and for smaller losses from other foods (equivalent on average to about 20 per cent loss overall); those for vitamin C from fresh green vegetables and other vegetables allow for losses of 75 and 50 per cent respectively.

Source: National Food Survey Data, MAFF (1988).

APPENDIX V
COMPOSITION OF VEGETABLES PER 100 G

(Sample data from McCance and Widdowson's *The Composition of Foods*)

No.	Food	Description and number of samples	Edible matter, proportion of weight purchased	Water g	Sugars g	Starch g	Dietary fibre g	Total nitrogen g
587	**Carrots, old** raw	Flesh only	0.96	89.9	5.4	0	2.9	0.11
588	boiled	Flesh only; cut up and boiled 45 minutes	0.87	91.5	4.2	0.1	3.1	0.10
589	**young** boiled	Purchased with leaves; flesh only, boiled 25 minutes	0.50	91.1	4.4	0.1	3.0	0.14
590	canned	6 samples; drained contents	0.63	91.2	4.4	Tr	3.7	0.11
591	**Cauliflower** raw	16 cauliflowers; flower and stalk	0.62	92.7	1.5	Tr	2.1	0.30
592	boiled	16 cauliflowers; flower and stalk, boiled 20 minutes	0.60	94.5	0.8	Tr	1.8	0.26
593	**Celeriac** boiled	Flesh only; boiled 30 minutes	0.79	90.2	1.5	0.5	4.9	0.26
594	**Celery** raw	Stem only	0.73	93.5	1.2	0.1	1.8	0.15
595	boiled	Stem only; boiled 30 minutes	0.72	95.7	0.7	0	2.2	0.10
596	**Chicory** raw	Stem and young leaves	0.79	96.2	—	0	—	0.12
597	**Cucumber** raw	Flesh only	0.77	96.4	1.8	0	0.4	0.10
598	**Endive** raw	Leaves only	0.63	93.7	1.0	0	2.2	0.28
599	**Horseradish** raw	Flesh of root	0.45	74.7	7.3	3.7	8.3	0.72
600	**Laverbread**	6 samples; cooked puréed seaweed coated in oatmeal	1.00	87.7	Tr	1.6	3.1	0.51
601	**Leeks** raw	Bulb only	0.36	86.0	6.0	0	3.1	0.31
602	boiled	Bulb only; boiled 30 minutes	0.44	90.8	4.6	0	3.9	0.28
603	**Lentils** raw	As purchased	1.00	12.2	2.4	50.8	11.7	3.80
604	split, boiled	As purchased; boiled 20 minutes	3.27	72.1	0.8	16.2	3.7	1.22
605	masur dahl, cooked	Recipe p. 344	—	78.4	0.7	10.7	2.4	0.78

Proximate and inorganic constituents per 100 g

No.	Food	Energy value		Protein (N × 6.25)	Fat	Carbo-hydrate	Na	K	Ca	Mg	P	Fe	Cu	Zn	S	Cl
		kcal	kJ	g	g	g						mg				
587	**Carrots, old** raw	23	98	0.7	Tr	5.4	95	220	48	12	21	0.6	0.08	0.4	7	69
588	boiled	19	79	0.6	Tr	4.3	50	87	37	6	17	0.4	0.08	0.3	5	31
589	**young** boiled	20	87	0.9	Tr	4.5	23	240	29	8	30	0.4	0.08	0.3	9	28
590	canned	19	82	0.7	Tr	4.4	280	84	27	5	15	1.3	0.04	0.3	—	450
591	**Cauliflower** raw	13	56	1.9	Tr	1.5	8	350	21	14	45	0.5	(0.03)	0.3	—	31
592	boiled	9	40	1.6	Tr	0.8	4	180	18	8	32	0.4	(0.03)	0.2	—	14
593	**Celeriac** boiled	14	59	1.6	Tr	2.0	28	400	47	12	71	0.8	0.13	—	13	23
594	**Celery** raw	8	36	0.9	Tr	1.3	140	280	52	10	32	0.6	0.11	0.1	15	180
595	boiled	5	21	0.6	Tr	0.7	67	130	52	9	19	0.4	0.11	0.1	8	100
596	**Chicory** raw	9	38	0.8	Tr	1.5a	7	180	18	13	21	0.7	0.14	0.2	13	25
597	**Cucumber** raw	10	43	0.6	0.1	1.8	13	140	23	9	24	0.3	0.09	0.1	11	25
598	**Endive** raw	11	47	1.8	Tr	1.0	10	380	44	10	67	2.8	0.09	—	26	71
599	**Horseradish** raw	59	253	4.5	Tr	11.0	8	580	120	36	70	2.0	0.14	—	210	19
600	**Laverbread**	52	217	3.2	3.7	1.6	560	220	20	31	51	3.5	0.12	0.8	—	820
601	**Leeks** raw	31	128	1.9	Tr	6.0	9	310	63	10	43	1.1	0.10	(0.1)	—	43
602	boiled	24	104	1.8	Tr	4.6	6	280	61	13	28	2.0	0.09	(0.1)	49	43
603	**Lentils** raw	304	1293	23.8	1.0	53.2	36	670	39	77	240	7.6	0.58	3.1	120	64
604	split, boiled	99	420	7.6	0.5	17.0	12	210	13	25	77	2.4	0.19	1.0	39	20
605	masur dahl, cooked	90	380	4.9	3.1	11.4	320	150	11	17	52	1.7	0.12	0.6	28	490

213

Vitamins per 100 g

No.	Food	Retinol µg	Carotene µg	Vitamin D µg	Thiamin mg	Riboflavin mg	Nicotinic acid mg	Potential nicotinic acid from tryptophan mg Trp ÷ 60	Vitamin C mg	Vitamin E mg
587	**Carrots, old** raw	0	12 000 (10 000–14 000)	0	0.06	0.05	0.6	0.1	6	0.5
588	boiled	0	12 000 (10 000–14 000)	0	0.05	0.04	0.4	0.1	4 (4–10)	0.5
589	**young** boiled	0	6000 (5000–7000)	0	0.05	0.04	0.4	0.1	4 (2–6)	0.5
590	canned	0	7000	0	0.04	0.02	0.3	0.1	3 (2–6)	(0.5)
591	**Cauliflower** raw	0	30 (6–50)	0	0.10	0.10	0.6	0.5	60 (50–90)	0.2ᵃ
592	boiled	0	30 (6–50)	0	0.06	0.06	0.4	0.4	20 (15–40)	0.1ᵇ
593	**Celeriac** boiled	0	0	0	0.04	0.04	0.5	0.3	4	—
594	**Celery** raw	0	Tr	0	0.03	0.03	0.3	0.2	7	0.2
595	boiled	0	Tr	0	0.02	0.02	0.2	0.1	5	0.2
596	**Chicory** raw	0	Tr	0	0.05	0.05	0.5	0.1	4	
597	**Cucumber** raw	0	Tr	0	0.04	0.04	0.2	0.1	8	Tr
598	**Endive** raw	0	2000 (1000–6000)	0	0.06	0.10	0.4	0.3	12	—
599	**Horseradish** raw	0	0	0	0.05	0.03	0.5	0.7	120	—
600	**Laverbread**	0	—	0	0.03	0.10	0.6	0.5	5	1.1
601	**Leeks** raw	0	40ᶜ	0	0.10	0.05	0.6	0.3	18 (15–30)	0.8
602	boiled	0	40ᶜ	0	0.07	0.03	0.4	0.3	15 (10–25)	0.8
603	**Lentils** raw	0	60	0	0.50	0.20	2.0	3.8	Tr	—
604	split, boiled	0	20	0	0.11	0.04	0.4	1.2	Tr	—
605	masur dahl, cooked	27	30	0.03	0.07	0.03	0.3	0.8	Tr	—

ᵃ This vegetable contains inulin; 50 per cent total carbohydrate taken to be available.

214

Vitamins per 100 g contd

No.	Food	Vitamin B_6 mg	Vitamin B_{12} µg	Folic acid Free µg	Folic acid Total µg	Pantothenic acid mg	Biotin µg
587	**Carrots, old** raw	0.15	0	12	15	0.25	0.6
588	boiled	0.09	0	1	8	0.18	0.4
589	**young** boiled	0.09	0	1	8	0.18	0.4
590	canned	0.02	0	1	7	0.10	0.4
591	**Cauliflower** raw	0.20	0	30	39	0.60	1.5
592	boiled	0.12	0	2	49	0.42	1.0
593	**Celeriac** boiled	0.10	0	—	—	—	—
594	**Celery** raw	0.10	0	6	12	0.40	0.1
595	boiled	0.06	0	(1)	(6)	0.28	Tr
596	**Chicory** raw	0.05	0	33	52	—	—
597	**Cucumber** raw	0.04	0	14	16	0.30	(0.4)
598	**Endive** raw	—	0	62	330	—	—
599	**Horseradish** raw	0.15	0	—	—	—	—
600	**Laverbread**	—	0	8	47	—	—
601	**Leeks** raw	0.25	0	—	—	0.12	1.4
602	boiled	0.15	0	7	—	0.10	1.0
603	**Lentils** raw	0.60	0	25	35	1.36	—
604	split, boiled	0.11	0	1	5	0.31	—
605	masur dahl, cooked	0.07	0	1	4	0.20	—

[a] Also contains 0.2 mg γ-tocopherol per 100 g.
[b] Also contains 0.1 mg γ-tocopherol per 100 g.
[c] Bulb only. The leaves contain about 2000 µg.

Source: McCance and Widdowson, *Composition of Foods*, Southgate, D. A. T., and Paul, A. (eds), 4th revised edition, London, HMSO, 1978.

215

APPENDIX VI
WEST MIDLANDS REGIONAL HEALTH AUTHORITY

FORM A

Tender for the supply of .... to NHS Authorities
.... 198 .... to .... 198 ....
NAME OF COMPANY ....

GUIDANCE FOR COMPLETING FORMS B AND C
Declaration of ingredient content and nutritional analysis of products
Both Form B and Form C should be completed for products for which samples and/or tenders are being submitted.
Form B
The nutritional data supplied should apply to the composition of the samples provided for evaluation and the products for which tenders are being submitted. Nutritional values analysed on an earlier formulation are not acceptable.
Use of laboratory methods of analysis is preferred.
If the product(s) for which a tender is submitted require further processing by the caterer, e.g. dehydrated mixes, two sets of nutritional data are required: These should be given on separate forms:
  (i) Nutritional data on products as supplied.
  (ii) Nutritional data on products reconstituted according to the instructions provided with the product.
The amounts declared should not differ from the actual energy and nutrient value of the products by more than can be justified by the nature and variability of the specific ingredients that make up the product in question. Under- or over-estimation are not to be used.
  Group A nutrients
  Data must be given for each of the Group A nutrients. If a nutrient is absent from a product, or present only in minimal quantities, please indicate this by using '0' or 'trace' as appropriate. Do not leave blank or use a dash (–).
  Group B nutrients
  Data should be given for the following vitamins and/or minerals for the products submitted for this tender.
....
If data is available for the other vitamins and minerals in Group B, these may be stated. Otherwise leave the columns blank.
In the event of the tender being accepted, data for all Group B nutrients will be required for all products accepted against the contract.
Form C
This is required for all products for which a sample is submitted for evaluation.
In the event of a tender being successful a declaration on composition and nutritional values will be required for all products accepted against the contract.
Please note the instructions at the foot of form C that percentage amounts of each ingredient are required to the first decimal point. Quantities need not be stated for ingredients amounting to less than 1.0 per cent.

FORM B

WEST MIDLANDS REGIONAL HEALTH AUTHORITY

Tender for the supply of _____ to NHS Authorities _____ 198_ to _____ 198_

NAME OF COMPANY _____

DECLARATION OF TYPICAL NUTRITIONAL ANALYSIS
COMPOSITION OF PRODUCTS per 100 g

For dehydrated mixes please indicate whether this chart refers to 1. Dry Mix *or* 2. Reconstituted product

Please see attached Form 'A' for guidance on completing this Form.

			GROUP A											
Product description	Energy value K cal	Protein g	Fat total g	Saturated g	Fatty acids Transun-saturated g	Polyun-saturated g	Carbohydrate total g	Total added sugars g	Added sucrose g	Dietary fibre g	Potassium mg	Sodium total mg	Added sodium chloride mg	Water %
Laboratory analysis*														
Food tables*														

				GROUP B						
Product description	Vit A iu	Thiamin mg	Riboflavin mg	Niacin mg	Folic acid Free µg	Folic acid Total µg	Vit B$_{12}$ µg	Vit C mg	Vit D iu	Calcium mg	Iron mg

*Method for obtaining nutritional data – please place a tick (✓) against laboratory analysis *or* against food tables as appropriate for each nutrient.

ADDITIONAL INFORMATION

1. If laboratory analysis method used for dietary fibre, please state method _____

2. If food tables other than McCance and Widdowson's *Composition of Foods* (1978) used, please list sources on separate sheet.

3. Do the products when reconstituted require the addition of any ingredients other than water? Yes/No

4. If Yes, are these additional ingredients included in the nutritional values for the reconstituted products? Yes/No

5. Date(s) analyses undertaken _____ Signed _____ Position in Company _____

FORM C

Tender for the supply of .... to NHS Authorities
.... 198 .... to .... 198 ....
NAME OF COMPANY ....

DECLARATION OF COMPOSITION OF PRODUCTS

The ingredients and nutritional analysis of each product for which a tender is submitted should be declared. Pre-printed literature may be submitted for ingredients provided it includes all the information listed below. The attached form 'Declaration of typical nutritional analysis' must be used for the nutritional data.

Product description	Ingredients	% of each ingredient of total	Country of origin if outside UK	Method of analysis*

For per cent of each ingredient please give figure to first decimal point.

Please list all ingredients including all sugars, salt, monosodium glutamate and additives. Please also include the serial number for each additive.

*If the nutritional composition for the product (listed separately) was arrived at by separate analysis of all or some of the ingredients, please indicate against each of these ingredients the method used i.e. LA for laboratory analysis or FT for food tables.

Date .... Signed ....
Position in Company ....

APPENDIX VII
USEFUL ADDRESSES FOR INFORMATION ON SPECIAL DIETS

British Dietetic Association
Daimler House
Paradise Circus, Queensway
Birmingham B1 2BJ

Coeliac Society
PO Box 181
London NW2 2QY

Vegetarian Society
53 Marloes Road
London W8 6LA

Catering and Dietetic Branch DOH
Hannibal House
Elephant and Castle
London SE1 6TE

The Sikh Cultural Society of
Great Britain
88 Mollison Way, Edgware
Middlesex HA8 5QN

The Chief Rabbi, Beth Din
Adler House
Tavistock Square
London WC1H 9HP

Health Education Authority
Hamilton House
Mabledon Place
London WC1A 9BD

British Diabetic Association
10 Queen Anne Street
London W1M 0BD

Vegan Society
33–35 George Street
Oxford OX1 2AY

The Islamic Foundation
223 London Road
Leicester LE2 1ZE

London Board for Schecita
Administrative Offices
1 Bridge Lane
Temple Fortune
Finchley Road
London NW11 0EA

APPENDIX VIII
RECIPE CONTRIBUTORS

Charles Boyd, Chester Boyd Ltd, Butcher's Hall, Bartholomew Close, Smithfield, London EC1A 7EB

Burley Manor Hotel & Restaurant, Burley Nr. Ringwood, New Forest, Hampshire BH24 4BS

Debbie Cooper, John Lewis Partnership, 12–14 Clipstone Street, London W1A 3AY

Hazel Coulbrough, Area Advisor in Dietetics, Grampian Health Board, Aberdeen and Sick Children's Hospital, Aberdeen

Julie Crouch, John Lewis, Milton Keynes

Mary Deans, Dietetic Lecturer, SHS School of Catering, Morningside Place, Edinburgh

East West Restaurant, 188 Old Street, London EC1V 9BP

Elsbeth Jaap, Student Dietetian, Aberdeen Royal Infirmary, Aberdeen

Angela Jacas, School Meals Training Officer, Education Dept, London Borough of Brent, 9 Park Lane, Wembley, London HA9 7RW

Jean-Claude Juston, The Cafe, London School of Economics, Houghton Street, London WC2

Robert Kelso, Leith's Good Food, 1 Sebastian Street, London EC1 0HE

Linda Lennison, Chestergate Pantry Vegetarian Eating Place & tea shop, 76 Chestergate, Macclesfield, Cheshire

Judith Liddel, ARA Offshore, 44 Carden Place, Aberdeen, Scotland AB1 1UP

John McManus, Four Seasons Chef, Inn on the Park, Hamilton Place, Park Lane, London W1A 1AZ

Mary Morgan, Catering Consultant, 78 Coleman Road, Fleckney, Leicestershire LE8 0BH

Moorland Links Hotel, Yelverton, South Devon PL20 6DA

Pauline Moore, St Mary's School, Douglas, Isle of Man

Deborah Parsons, Stuart Cabledu Catering Limited, 162–164 Arthur Road, Wimbledon Park, London SW19 8AH

Shirlee Posner, 12 Woodlands Park Road, London N15 3RT

L W Rivers, Catering Manager, The Slade Hospital, Headington, Oxford OX3 7JH

Rhonda Roberts, Ingleside, High Street, Auchenblae, Kincardineshire, Scotland AB3 1XR

Grahame Scholey, Food Industries Dept, Cassio College, Langley Road, Watford

Beverley Seward, Cook in Charge, Otley Street Nursery, Skipton, North Yorkshire

Lynn Taylor, Cook Supervisor, Graham School, Scarborough, North Yorkshire

Anne Turner, Compass Services Ltd, Queen's Wharf, Queen Caroline Street, London W6 9RJ

Miss H B Yeulett, Catering Manager, Hastings Health Authority, Royal East Sussex Hospital, Hastings TN34 1ER

INDEX

220

ACKNOWLEDGEMENTS

Like folk songs and the best recipes, this book owes a debt to many influences which are often difficult to identify and usually easy to underestimate. Most of my colleagues in nutrition, food policy, and catering have had their effects, often without their knowing. I wish to thank in particular Alison Dobson, Freda Eskin, Brian Saunders, Herbie Davies, Mary Morgan, Debbie Cooper, Rodney Stead, Anne Turner, Shirlee Posner, Miriam Polunin, Linda Wood, Caroline Waldegrave who contributed through various combinations of advice, reading drafts, and recipe testing: Michael Crawford and Wendy Doyle at the Nuffield Institute of Comparative Medicine carried out the nutritional analyses of the recipes: Richard Foulsham and Lindsey Temple at Evian Agencies UK and Joe Hyam, editor of the *Caterer and Hotelkeeper* magazine, for their sponsorship and support: Jill Norman for her efficient and sympathetic editing of the manuscript.

The publishers would like to thank Paris-Kerr for the photographs. The extracts from 'McCance and Widdowson's The Composition of Foods', 'Recommended Daily Amounts of Nutrients' and 'National Food Survey Data (MAFF), 1988' are reproduced with permission of the Controller of Her Majesty's Stationery Office.

REFERENCES AND GENERAL READING

Health Education Authority *Guide to healthy eating*
Holland, B., Unwin, I. D. and Buss, D. (1988), *Cereals and cereal products: the third supplement to McCance and Widdowson's The Composition of Foods (4th edition)*, Nottingham: Royal Society of Chemistry, MAFF
MAFF (1976), *Manual of Nutrition*, London: HMSO
Morse, E., Rivers, J., Heughan, A. (1988), *Food and Health*, London: Barrie and Jenkins
Passmore, R. (1980), 'An historical introduction to food, health and nutrition policies in the United Kingdom', in *Nutrition in the Community*, ed. D. S. McLaren, Chichester, Wiley, pp. 19–50
Paul, A. A. and Southgate, D. A. T. (1974), *McCance and Widdowson's Composition of Foods*, London: HMSO
RCP (1983), 'Obesity: a report of the Royal College of Physicians', *J. Roy. Coll. Phy.*, 17:3–58
Robbins, C. J. (1985), *Eating for Health*, London: Granada
Wenlock, R. W., Disselduff, M. M., Skinner, R. K., Knight, I. (unpublished), 'The Diets of British Schoolchildren', study conducted by the DHSS in 1985